CONTENTS

FAMILY GUY

INTRO-DUCTION

GOOD DAY TO YOU FELLOW FAMILY GUY, GAL OR GAY,

CONGRATULATIONS! WHAT YOU HOLD IN YOUR, VERY PROBABLY, SWEATY HAND IS THE 2010 FAMILY GUY ANNUAL.

IF HOWEVER YOU ARE READING THIS SECOND HAND AFTER IT WAS WRONGLY DISCARDED AS SUB-STANDARD BY A MORE CONSERVATIVE PERSON YOU ONCE CONSIDERED AS FAMILY OR FRIEND, OR IT WAS MISTAKEN AS AN ANIMATED VERSION OF THE GIDEON'S BIBLEL, SHAME ON YOU. AND SHAME ON YOUR FAMILY FOR NOT RECOGNISING THAT YOU NOW QUITE HAPPILY LOITER ON SOCIETY'S MARGINS.

IF THIS IS THE FIRST TIME YOU'VE EVER PICKED UP A PIECE OF FAMILY GUY LITERATURE WHERE HAVE YOU BEEN? YOU ARE IN FOR QUITE AN EYE-OPENER. THE SORT OF EYE-OPENER THAT WOULD MAKE EVEN GOGGLE-EYED MARTI FELDMAN THINK: 'MY, HIS EYES HAVE REALLY BEEN OPENED'. HERE'S THE GIG. FAMILY GUY FOLLOWS THE ADVENTURES OF LOVABLE OAF PETER GRIFFIN VOICED BY THE, FRANKLY HILARIOUSLY HANDSOME SETH MACFARLANE AND HIS HILARIOUSLY ODD FAMILY OF MIDDLE-CLASS NEW ENGLANDERS, THE GRIFFINS.

PETER IS A MAN WHO BELIEVES IN THE VERY CREATIVE MAXIM OF SPEAK BEFORE YOU THINK: "JUST DON'T FORGET OUR DEAL, LOIS. I SIT THROUGH THIS AND LATER TONIGHT I GET ANAL. YOU HEAR ME? NO MATTER HOW NEAT I WANT THE HOUSE YOU HAVE TO CLEAN IT."

PETER'S WIFE LOIS, VOICED BY ALEX BORSTEIN, IS A FORMER MISS TEEN RHODE ISLAND WHO RULES THE ROOST WHILE REMAINING BUT A STEP AWAY FROM A NERVOUS BREAKDOWN. SHE CAN CALCULATE THE STREET VALUE OF A DRUGS STASH WITH UNERRING, DISTURBING EASE AND SINGS SWING LIKE IT AINT NO THING.

PETER AND LOIS HAVE THREE CHILDREN, MEG, A FRUMPY TEENAGER WHO IS VOICED BY MILA KUNIS AND ACTS AS THE FAMILY'S SUICIDAL PUNCH BAG. THEN THERE'S MIDDLE CHILD CHRIS WHO HAS INHERITED HIS FATHER'S INFINITE STUPIDITY WHILE CONCEALING AN IMPRESSIVE, AND DIVERSE, ARTISTIC ABILITY. ONE-YEAR-OLD STEWIE IS DIABOLICALLY CLEVER, CONSTANTLY PLOTTING WAYS TO KILL HIS MOTHER AND FINALLY UNEARTH THE QUESTION, WHY DOES MEN'S AFTERSHAVE SMELL JUST SOOOOOO GOOOOOD? FINALLY, DRAGGING HIS WORM-RIDDEN BEHIND ALONG THE FAMILY RUG IS BRIAN. THOUGH JUST A DOG, BRIAN IS A MEMBER OF MENSA, LOVES MARTINIS, DUMB BLONDES, MARIJUANA AND STICKS.

SO FAR SO PLAIN SAILING. BUT YOU KNOW, WHILE LUKE HAS DARTH, SHERLOCK HAS MORIARTY AND MUSICAL CREDIBILITY HAS JUSTIN TIMBERLAKE SO EACH OF OUR HEROES HAS THEIR NEMESIS. FOR PETER, ERNIE THE CHICKEN BURSTS INTO RANDOM EPISODES FOR RANDOM FISTICUFFS IN RANDOM PLACES, LOIS' PIANO TEACHING RIVAL ALEXIS RADCLIFFE PLAYS SUPERBLY WITH A MINOR, AN EVIL MONKEY LIVES IN CHRIS' CLOSET, CONNIE D'AMICO, THE MOST POPULAR GIRL IN SCHOOL, LIVES IN MEG'S NIGHTMARES AND THE LAST OF PETER'S SPERM BECOMES BERTRAM, A WHINIER VERSION OF STEWIE, BORN BY LESBIAN, WHO WILL NOT REST UNTIL HE GAINS CONTROL OF THE SCHOOL PLAYGROUND. YOU GET THE IDEA: SOMEWHERE TO GO WHEN SCRIPTWRITERS RUN OUT OF IDEAS.

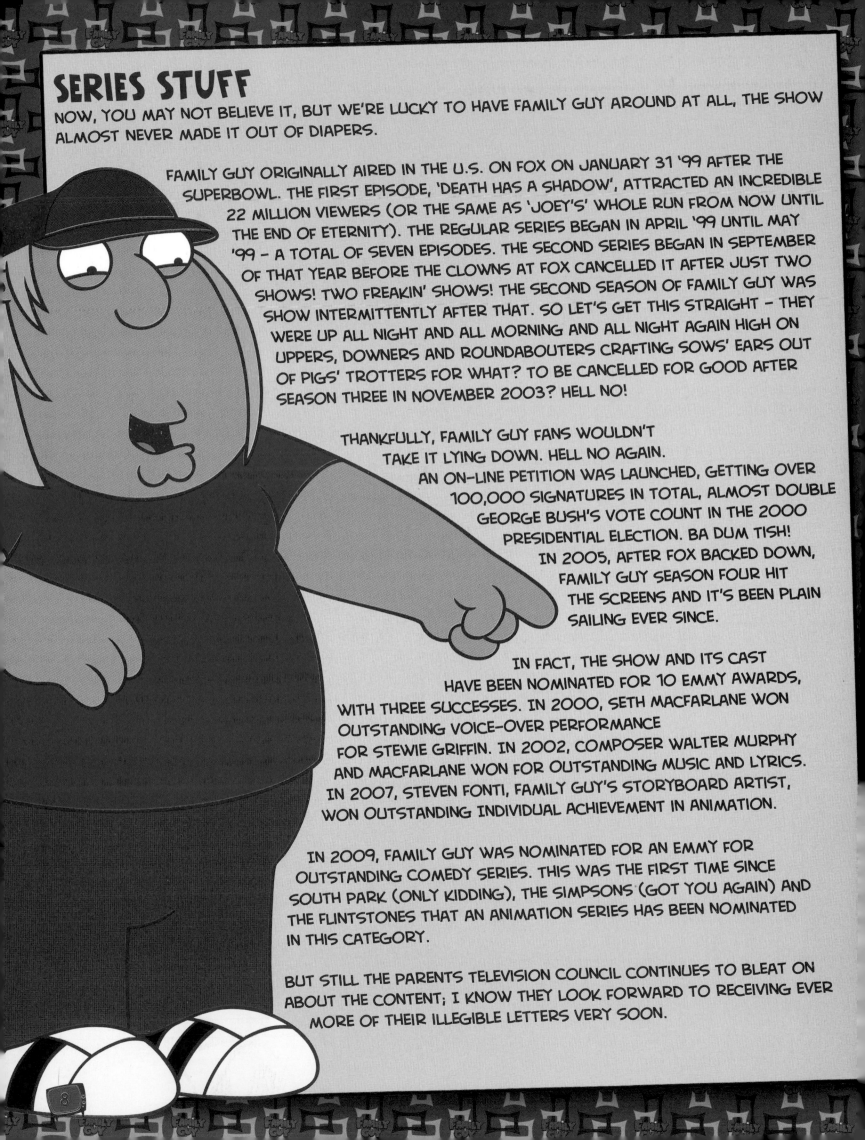

SERIES STUFF

NOW, YOU MAY NOT BELIEVE IT, BUT WE'RE LUCKY TO HAVE FAMILY GUY AROUND AT ALL, THE SHOW ALMOST NEVER MADE IT OUT OF DIAPERS.

FAMILY GUY ORIGINALLY AIRED IN THE U.S. ON FOX ON JANUARY 31 '99 AFTER THE SUPERBOWL. THE FIRST EPISODE, 'DEATH HAS A SHADOW', ATTRACTED AN INCREDIBLE 22 MILLION VIEWERS (OR THE SAME AS 'JOEY'S' WHOLE RUN FROM NOW UNTIL THE END OF ETERNITY). THE REGULAR SERIES BEGAN IN APRIL '99 UNTIL MAY '99 - A TOTAL OF SEVEN EPISODES. THE SECOND SERIES BEGAN IN SEPTEMBER OF THAT YEAR BEFORE THE CLOWNS AT FOX CANCELLED IT AFTER JUST TWO SHOWS! TWO FREAKIN' SHOWS! THE SECOND SEASON OF FAMILY GUY WAS SHOW INTERMITTENTLY AFTER THAT. SO LET'S GET THIS STRAIGHT - THEY WERE UP ALL NIGHT AND ALL MORNING AND ALL NIGHT AGAIN HIGH ON UPPERS, DOWNERS AND ROUNDABOUTERS CRAFTING SOWS' EARS OUT OF PIGS' TROTTERS FOR WHAT? TO BE CANCELLED FOR GOOD AFTER SEASON THREE IN NOVEMBER 2003? HELL NO!

THANKFULLY, FAMILY GUY FANS WOULDN'T TAKE IT LYING DOWN. HELL NO AGAIN. AN ON-LINE PETITION WAS LAUNCHED, GETTING OVER 100,000 SIGNATURES IN TOTAL, ALMOST DOUBLE GEORGE BUSH'S VOTE COUNT IN THE 2000 PRESIDENTIAL ELECTION. BA DUM TISH! IN 2005, AFTER FOX BACKED DOWN, FAMILY GUY SEASON FOUR HIT THE SCREENS AND IT'S BEEN PLAIN SAILING EVER SINCE.

IN FACT, THE SHOW AND ITS CAST HAVE BEEN NOMINATED FOR 10 EMMY AWARDS, WITH THREE SUCCESSES. IN 2000, SETH MACFARLANE WON OUTSTANDING VOICE-OVER PERFORMANCE FOR STEWIE GRIFFIN. IN 2002, COMPOSER WALTER MURPHY AND MACFARLANE WON FOR OUTSTANDING MUSIC AND LYRICS. IN 2007, STEVEN FONTI, FAMILY GUY'S STORYBOARD ARTIST, WON OUTSTANDING INDIVIDUAL ACHIEVEMENT IN ANIMATION.

IN 2009, FAMILY GUY WAS NOMINATED FOR AN EMMY FOR OUTSTANDING COMEDY SERIES. THIS WAS THE FIRST TIME SINCE SOUTH PARK (ONLY KIDDING), THE SIMPSONS (GOT YOU AGAIN) AND THE FLINTSTONES THAT AN ANIMATION SERIES HAS BEEN NOMINATED IN THIS CATEGORY.

BUT STILL THE PARENTS TELEVISION COUNCIL CONTINUES TO BLEAT ON ABOUT THE CONTENT; I KNOW THEY LOOK FORWARD TO RECEIVING EVER MORE OF THEIR ILLEGIBLE LETTERS VERY SOON.

THE CLAM CLAN

IT'S NOT JUST THE GRIFFINS THAT THOSE ON THE MORAL GRASSY KNOLL OBJECT TO, QUAHOG HAS AN EVER-GROWING COMMUNITY OF DEVIANTS TO TARGET.

PETER'S CLOSE FRIEND QUAGMIRE IS 'AN APPALLING HUMAN BEING WHO IS STILL CAUGHT IN THE RAT-PACK ERA'. ALMOST EVERYTHING IN QUAGMIRE'S HOUSE FOLDS OUT INTO A BED WHILE HE FIND SEXUAL EXCITEMENT IN ALMOST EVERYTHING, APART FROM THE USE OF THE WORD 'RUBBISH' TO MEAN 'GARBAGE'.

PETER AND QUAGMIRE'S FRIEND, CLEVELAND, OWNS A DELICATESEN, 'CLEVELAND'S DELI'. CLEVELAND USED TO USE HIS VOICE LIKE A MACHINE GUN AT A LOCAL AUCTION BEFORE A TOTEM POLE HIT HIM ON THE HEAD. HIS SPEECH IS NOW DULL AND MONOTONOUS LIKE ANYTHING JIM CARREY IS IN WHERE HE ISN'T ACTING LIKE HE'S HIGH ON CRACK.

PETER AND QUAGMIRE AND CLEVELAND'S FRIEND, OVER-ENTHUSIASTIC EX-WALKER JOE SWANSON, RECEIVED HIS PARALYZING INJURY AT CHRISTMAS TIME WHILE INVESTING INVESTIGATING A ROBBERY AT AN ORPHANAGE, COMMITTED BY A GRINCH. JOE SLID OFF THE ROOF ON A ROLLER SKATE, INJURING HIS SPINE AND LEAVING HIM UNABLE TO WALK. DESPITE HIS 'HANDICAP', HE 'SERVES' ON THE POLICE FORCE, 'CHOREOGRAPHS' LOCAL MUSICALS AND 'DRIVES'.

THESE FOUR FELLAS ARE THE FAMILY GUY BARBER STRING QUARTET ON WHICH THE FAMILY GUY HIGH JINKS ARE ACCOMPANIED, BUT THERE'S MORE, OH SO MUCH MORE...

AT QUAHOG'S CHANNEL 5 NEWS TELEVISION STATION THERE'S NARCISSISTIC ANCHORMAN TOM TUCKER AND HIS WELL-PROPORTIONED SIDE KICK DIANE SIMMONS. ONCE, AFTER TOM LIED ABOUT THE LAST WILLIE WONKA-SILVER-TICKET TYPE PAWTUCKET SCROLL (WHICH ALLOWED THE FINDER AN EXCLUSIVE TRIP AROUND THE PAWTUCKET BREWERY) BEING FOUND, HE CONFESSED: "THAT'S RIGHT, I MADE IT UP. I FIGURED IF PEOPLE THOUGHT THE LAST SCROLL WAS FOUND, EVERYONE WOULD STOP LOOKING, GIVING ME THE EDGE TO FIND IT MYSELF. WHAT I DID WAS WRONG... AND AS AN ACT OF CONTRITION, I WILL NOW INSERT THIS CARNIVOROUS EARWIG INTO MY BRAIN... HEH... KINDA TICKLES... (INHALES DEEPLY THROUGH THE NOSE) AHH!!! AHH!!! OH GOD!!! IT'S EATING OUT THE BACK OF MY EYES!!! AHH!!!" YOU GET THE IDEA.

THERE'S MAYOR ADAM WEST, VOICED BY FORMER BATMAN, ERM, ADAM WEST. HE ONCE SPENT $1,000 INVESTIGATING WHO WAS STEALING HIS WATER, IT TURNED OUT TO BE HIS DAMN PLUG HOLE. HE PLANTED 'SAUSAGE SEEDS' AND CELEBRATED WILDLY WHEN THEY WORKED (IT LATER TURNED OUT BRIAN HAD BEEN 'SOILING' HIS LAWN.)

THERE'S HERBERT, THE GRIFFIN'S 'FRIENDLY', WHISTLY-VOICED OLD NEIGHBOUR, WHO HAS A SWEET SPOT FOR CHRIS AND A DAMP SPOT FOR CHRIS. HE ALSO HAS A WHOLE BUNCH OF POPSICLES IN HIS BASEMENT FOR SEXY YOUNG PAPERBOYS TO COME DOWN AND TRY. AWAY FROM THE REAL WORLD, THERE'S GOD, SATAN, DEATH AND DEATH DOG VYING FOR THE SOULS OF THE LIVING ALONGSIDE A SLEW OF CELEBRITIES WHO'D GLEEFULLY USE THEIR DYING GRANDMOTHER AS A HUMAN SHIELD AGAINST A THROB OF BAD-MOUTHED, GUN-TOTIN', BIKINI-WEARIN' POLICEWOMEN.

BUT THERE'S BEEN A SLEW OF CELEBRITIES APPEAR ON FAMILY GUY THAT ARE EVEN BIGGER THAN TED DANSON.

DREW BARRYMORE PROVIDES THE VOICE OF BRIAN'S ON AND OFF GIRLFRIEND JILLIAN; ROBERT DOWNEY JR PLAYS LOIS' BROTHER, STRANGLER EXTRAORDINAIRE, PATRICK; ROB LOWE THEIR NEIGHBOUR STANFORD CORDRAY; WHILE WILL FERRELL, KIEFER SUTHERLAND, JAMES WOODS AND KISS ARE REGULARS ON THE SHOW.

YOU KNOW, WE LIKE TO THINK THAT IF YOUR TELEVISION COULD TALK IT WOULD SAY THANK YOU, THANK YOU OH LORD OF THE CONTROL, THANK YOU FOR FILLING UP MY CHEST WITH IMAGES OF INSANITY AND MIRTH.

BUT BEFORE YOU CONTINUE READING THIS YEAR'S COLLECTION OF ANECDOTES, ANAL JOKES, PROFILES AND PROFANITY WE'D LIKE TO SAY ONE LAST THING.

YOU ARE FEELING SLEEPY, VERY, VERY SLEEPY, YOU ARE FEELING VERY, VERY RELAXED, YOU ARE SLOWLY FALLING BACKWARDS INTO A DEEP, DEEP SLEEP... WHEN YOU AWAKE YOU WILL EMPTY YOUR BANK ACCOUNT AND BUY ALL SEVEN OF THE FAMILY GUY SEASONAL DVDS, YOU WILL BUY A SELECTION OF ILL-FITTING FAMILY GUY T-SHIRTS, YOU WILL BUY A LIMITED EDITION 'I LOVE STEWIE' MEDALLION, HELL, YOU WILL EVEN GET HOLD OF SOME OF THE UNOFFICIAL STUFF JUST TO FUND ILLEGAL CRIME. WHEN YOU COME BACK INTO THE ROOM YOU WILL LAUGH RAUCOUSLY AT EVERY ATTEMPT WE MAKE AT HUMOUR AND EMBARRASS YOURSELF AND THE REST OF THE ROOM BY BLURTING OUT THE MOST INAPPROPRIATE ELEMENTS OF THIS ANNUAL TO THE MOST FRAGILE MEMBER IN THE ROOM. WAKE UP!

HEY, WE REALLY HOPE YOU ENJOY THE FAMILY GUY 2010 ANNUAL AND THAT YOU FEEL COMPLETELY FULFILLED BY SANTA'S HAIRY SACK OF MAGIC. MERRY FREAKIN' CHRISTMAS.

PETER
PROFILE & GRIFFIN INTERVIEW

AW, CRAP!

PETER GRIFFIN

PETER ASSERTS THAT THE BIRD IS, IN FACT, THE WORD. HAVEN'T YOU HEARD? THE BIRD IS NOT GREATER OR LESS THAN THE WORD, IT IS THE WORD. JESUS IS ALSO THE WORD. WHICH MAKES JESUS A BIRD.

EDUCATION? PAH! PETER NEVER PASSED THE THIRD GRADE BUT DID THAT STOP HIM FLYING THE SPACE SHUTTLE? OR BECOMINGA COWBOY? OR ORGANISING GLADIATOR MICE?

THE SELF-APPOINTED MASTER OF THE TV REMOTE CONTROL, PETER HAS AN INTELLECT THAT MAKES HIM MENTALLY RETARDED (BUT CLEVERER THA CREATIONISTS). EVER NOTICED PETER'S SHORT ATTENTION SPAN? EVER NOTICED PETER'S SHORT ATTENTION SPAN? I SAY, EVE NOTICED PETER'S SHORT ATTENTION SPAN?

REGRET? REGRET IS AN EMBARRASSING, HEAD-COVERING STRAWBERRY BIRTHMARK ON THE FACE OF PETER GRIFFIN.

FACTFILE

AGE: 42

PLACE OF BIRTH: MEXICO

BIRTH NAME: PETER LOWENBROU GRIFFIN

GENDER: ORANGUTAN

14

PETER'S MIDDLE NAME 'LOWENBROU', IS THE NAME OF A GERMAN BEER, WHICH DIRECTLY TRANSLATES TO 'LION'S BREW', HIS FAVOURITE ANIMAL AND DRINK. SOME CALL IT FATE.

PETER IS INCREDIBLY JEALOUS OF ANY MAN WHO FINDS LOIS ATTRACTIVE. HE ONCE PUNCHED HIS OWN REFLECTION IN A MIRROR AFTER LOIS DESCRIBED HIM AS HANDSOME.

PETER TRIED HINDUISM BUT WAS KICKED OUT AFTER TACKLING THE HINDU LEADER TO THE FLOOR – HE THOUGHT THE RED DOT ON HIS HEAD WAS A LASER SPOT FROM A SNIPER RIFLE.

PETER IS A COMMITTED DRINKER, HE IS ADDICTED TO CHEAP TELEVISION, CAN BE IMPULSIVE, THOUGHTLESS AND AT TIMES RECKLESS...

FUN FACTS

MEET... PETER GRIFFIN

PETER GRIFFIN IS A MAN WHO HAS A DEEP AND LOYAL COMMITMENT TO DRINKING AND AN ADMIRABLE ADDICTION TO CHEAP TELEVISION. HE'S A MAN WHO IS IMPULSIVE, THOUGHTLESS AND RECKLESS – OR, TO PUT IT ANOTHER WAY, A REAL MAN'S MAN.

HE MAY WELL HAVE AN IQ SCORE THAT PLACES HIM JUST BELOW MENTALLY RETARDED, BUT HE'S FAT, LOVEABLE, AND LOVES PAWTUCKET BEER.

HE USED TO WORK AT A TOY FACTORY, THEN AS A FISHERMAN AND EVENTUALLY LANDED A JOB AT HIS FAVOURITE BREWERY. THAT'S NOT INCLUDING THE MANY OTHER JOBS HE HAD IN BETWEEN THOSE AS HE SEARCHED FOR A MEANING TO LIFE.

TECHNICALLY HE WAS BORN IN MEXICO BUT HE LOOKS ON HIMSELF AS 100 PER CENT AMERICAN AND A BIG PATRIOT. A COMMITTED FATHER WITH A HATE-HATE RELATIONSHIP WITH HIS TWO OLDER CHILDREN, HE'S ALSO A DEVOTED FRIEND TO BRIAN, THE FAMILY DOG.

THE LIFE AND TIMES OF PETER GRIFFIN

BONNIE: SOMEBODY SAVE HIM, HE CAN'T SWIM!

PETER: OH, HE'S NOT EVEN KICKING. KICK JOE, KICK.

LOIS: PETER, HE'S A PARAPLEGIC!

PETER: THAT DOESN'T MEAN HE CAN'T HEAR. KICK JOE, KICK.

PETER: I KNOW SOMETHING ABOUT STUPID PHONE CALLS

(PHONE RINGS IN HOUSE)

LOIS: HELLO?

PETER: I CANT TAKE THE TRASH OUT TODAY I'M WORKING LATE AT THE OFFICE.

LOIS: THE CALLED ID SAYS YOUR CALLING FROM THE KITCHEN. IN FACT I CAN SEE YOU.

PETER: CAN YOU SEE ME NOW?

LOIS: NO.

PETER: NOW I AM AT THE OFFICE.

LOIS: OKAY, ONE MORE MINUTE, AND THEN IF THERE ARE TWO PINK LINES...

PETER: OH GOD, I HOPE YOU'RE NOT PREGNANT, WE CAN'T AFFORD ANOTHER KID. WE ALREADY GOT CHRIS, STEWEY, RICHIE, JOANIE, GREG, MARSHA, BOBBY, JAN, MIKE SEAVER, CAROL SEAVER, BONER, URKEL, MR. FURLEY...

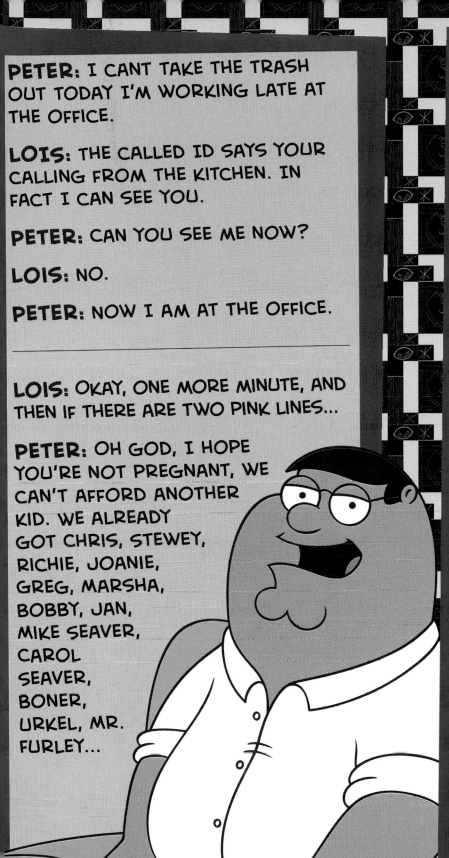

BRIAN: PETER THOSE AREN'T YOUR KIDS, THAT'S THE NICK-AT-NIGHT LINEUP.

PETER: BLANKA, ZANGEIF, CHUN-LI, GUILE, E. HONDA...

BRIAN: THAT'S STREET FIGHTER.

PETER: RED, BLUE, GREEN...

BRIAN: THOSE ARE COLOURS.

PETER: IT'S A BEAUTIFUL BABY GIRL!

CAROL: OH, A GIRL! I'M SO HAPPY!

PETER: BUT IT HAS A PENIS. (PICKS UP SCALPEL.) I'LL TAKE CARE OF THAT.

LOIS: PETER, NO!

PETER: (AFTER LOIS SAYS HE'S CHILDISH) "IF I'M A CHILD THAT MEANS YOU'RE A PAEDOPHILE, AND I'LL BE DAMNED IF I'M GOING STAND HERE AND TAKE THIS FROM A PERVERT."

LOIS: PETER, WHY ARE WE STOPPED?

PETER: YEAH, I'LL HAVE THREE CHEESEBURGERS...

LOIS: PETER FOR GOD'S SAKES SHE'S HAVIN' A BABY!

PETER: OH THAT'S RIGHT... AND A KID'S MEAL... AND I GUESS I'LL HAVE FRIES... IF I HAVE FRIES IS ANYONE ELSE GONNA HAVE ANY? I DON'T WANNA BE THE ONLY ONE EATIN' THEM... I'LL FEEL LIKE A FATTY.

PETER: I HAD SUCH A CRUSH ON HER. UNTIL I MET YOU LOIS. YOU'RE MY SILVER MEDAL.

PETER: HEY MORT, DO THESE SUPPOSITORIES COME IN OTHER FLAVOURS?

MORT: PETER, ARE YOU EATING THOSE?

PETER: NO, I'M SHOVING 'EM UP MY BUTT. OF COURSE I'M EATING 'EM!

PETER: (PHONE MESSAGE TO EMPLOYER) MR. WEED? THIS IS PETER GRIFFIN. I WILL NOT BE COMING TO WORK TODAY. I WAS IN A TERRIBLE PLANE CRASH. MY ENTIRE FAMILY WAS KILLED AND I AM A VEGETABLE.

DOCTOR: WAIT A MINUTE, BRIAN, YOU HAVE A PRE-EXISTING RELATIONSHIP WITH THIS DEGENERATE?

PETER: A DEGENERATE, AM I? WELL YOU ARE A FESTIZIO! SEE, I CAN MAKE UP WORDS TOO, SISTER.

CHRIS: HEY, DAD, LOOK! I COVERED MY BACK WITH HONEY AND NOW THE ANTS ARE TAKING ME HOME.

PETER: HE DOES THE SAME THING AT HOME WITH VELVEETA AND COCKROACHES. IF YOU TURN THE LIGHT ON REALLY FAST THEY SLAM HIM RIGHT INTO THE FRIDGE.

LOIS: PETER, DID YOU POST A NEW PICTURE OF YOURSELF ON OUR WEDDING PICTURE?

PETER: YEAH, I THINK IT LOOKS BETTER.

LOIS: YOU POSTED IT OVER ME!!

PETER: YEAH, I THINK IT LOOKS BETTER.

MEG: I FINALLY GET MY DRIVER'S LICENSE AND THE CAR GETS TAKEN AWAY, HOW IRONIC.

PETER: MEG, DON'T TALK TO YOUR MOTHER THAT WAY, SHE IS NOT AN IRON.

LOIS: PETER, THIS CAR HAS DENTS IN IT, AND IT'S GOT A CARDBOARD STEERING WHEEL. AND LOOK, THERE'S NO ENGINE! IT JUST HAS A DRAWING OF AN ENGINE!

CAR SALESMAN: BUT IT ONLY HAD ONE PREVIOUS OWNER... JAMES BOND!

PETER: I'LL TAKE IT!

LOIS: YOU GAVE UP A BOAT FOR FREE TICKETS TO A CRAPPY COMEDY CLUB!

PETER: COME ONE, LOIS, YOU'RE ACTING LIKE THIS IS THE FIRST TIME I EVER DID SOMETHING STUPID.

BARTENDER: YOU STILL OWE ME FOR THE OTHER ROUNDS, WHICH COMES TO 50 BUCKS.

PETER: I'M A FOREIGN DIPLOMAT. I DON'T PAY FOR DRINKS. DO YOU THINK G. GORDON LIDDY PAID FOR HIS DRINKS WHILE HE WAS STRANGLING PEOPLE WITH PIANO WIRE FOR THE GOOD OF OUR NATION?

QUAHOG, QUAHOG, QUAHOG,

WHERE THE HELL IS QUAHOG?

SOMETIMES YOU WANNA GO WHERE EVERYBODY KNOWS YOUR NAME... AND THEY'RE ALWAYS GLAD YOU CAME...

CHEERS! AND WELCOME TO QUAHOG, WHICH PERCHES ITS SUNSHINE-D SELF ON THE EAST COAST OF THE UNITED STATES OF YEEEEEEEEHAWWWWWW! IT SITS IN THE STATE OF RHODE ISLAND AND IS A FICTIONAL SUBURB OF A REAL CITY, PROVIDENCE. OR THERE AGAIN, IT MAY NOT BE.

WHY PROVIDENCE? WELL, THE SHOW'S ZEUS, SETH MACFARLANE, LIVED IN PROVIDENCE WHEN HE WAS A STUDENT AT THE RHODE ISLAND SCHOOL OF DESIGN.

THERE ARE CONSTANT REFERENCES TO THE PLACE IN THE SHOW, WITH ACTUAL, REAL BUILDINGS CONSTANTLY DRAWN INTO THE SCENERY. AND NAMES? THE SHOW OFTEN BORROWS THE NAMES OF RHODE ISLAND PLACES SUCH AS PAWTUCKET.

EVEN MORE INTERESTING, IF THAT WERE POSSIBLE, IS THAT SETH, IN AN INTERVIEW WITH ONE OF THOSE RADIO STATIONS THAT HAS LOADS OF LETTERS FOLLOWED BY A COUPLE OF NUMBERS (WNAC FOX 64 NEWS) SAID THAT QUAHOG WAS ACTUALLY MODELLED AFTER CRANSTON, RHODE ISLAND. DID YOU KNOW, OVER 30% OF CRANSTON'S RESIDENTS DESCRIBE THEMSELVES AS ITALIAN AMERICAN? THIS IS ONE OF THE HIGHEST PERCENTAGES OF THIS ETHNIC GROUP IN CITIES WITH OVER 50,000 RESIDENTS IN THE US! FORGET ABOUT IT.

WHAT WE DO KNOW IS THAT THE ONE FINANCIAL CENTER, 50 KENNEDY PLAZA, AND THE BANK OF AMERICA TOWER, ARE REGULARLY FEATURED IN FAMILY GUY. THESE REAL LANDMARKS POINT THE FINGER AT QUAHOG BEING WEST OF CENTRAL PROVIDENCE.

IF YOU'RE LOOKING TO FAMILY GUY WRITERS FOR A LITTLE CLARITY, LOOK AGAIN. ONE OF THE FEW MAPS SHOWING QUAHOG WAS IN 'E. PETERBUS UNUM'. WHEN QUAHOG 5 NEWS SHOWED A MAP OF RHODE ISLAND, WITH A DOT MARKING THE LOCATION OF PETORIA (THE COUNTRY FOUNDED BY PETER IN QUAHOG) THE DOT IS SHOWN IN AT LEAST THREE DIFFERENT PLACES. CONFUSED? US TOO!

AT LEAST WE CAN BE CLEAR ON THE HISTORY OF QUAHOG. ACCORDING TO MAYOR ADAM WEST, QUAHOG WAS FOUNDED BY A SAILOR OF A BOAT BOUND FOR NEW YORK WHO WAS THROWN OVERBOARD FOR HIS LOQUACIOUSNESS (THAT'S BEING TOO WORDY TO YOU, YOU SCHMUCK). A MAGICAL TALKING CLAM RESCUED HIM AND BROUGHT HIM TO SHORE AND TOGETHER THEY FOUNDED THE TOWN. DID YOU KNOW A QUAHOG IS A TYPE OF CLAM?

PETER'S ACCOUNT OF THE TOWN'S FOUNDING DIFFERS. HE STATES THAT QUAHOG WAS FOUNDED BY HIS ANCESTOR GRIFFIN PETERSON. HOLY. AND. CRAP.

JUST WALK AWAY.

NOTHING TO SEE HERE.

JUST KEEP WALKING BUDDY...

LOIS
PROFILE & GRIFFIN INTERVIEW

I am not a **CRAZY** *broad.*

23

LOIS GRIFFIN

LOIS WAS RAISED PROTESTANT, WHICH DIDN'T PLEASE PETER'S STAUNCH IRISH-CATHOLIC STEPFATHER, FRANCIS GRIFFIN. IN FACT, FRANCIS DESPISES LOIS. ON THEIR WEDDING DAY, HE SPRAY-PAINTED 'TO A PROTESTANT WHORE' UNDERNEATH THE 'JUST MARRIED' SIGN ON THE BACK OF THEIR CAR.

ONCE, IN A DREAM, LOIS FOUND STEWIE'S 'SECRET LAB' WHILE PUTTING AWAY CLOTHES. NOT THAT SHE'S A NOSEY MOTHER WHO GOES THROUGH HER CHILDREN'S LAUNDRY LOOKING FOR NOTES. OR READ MEG'S DIARY. OR GOES THROUGH PETER'S DROPPINGS.

LOIS' BROTHER, PATRICK PEWTERSCHMIDT, WAS IN A MENTAL ASYLUM FOR KILLING FAT PEOPLE. PATRICK WAS KNOWN AS 'THE FAT GUY STRANGLER'. CAN'T HAVE BEEN DIFFICULT, HAVE YOU EVER SEEN A FAT GUY TRY AND LOOK BEHIND HIMSELF? HIS NECK GETS ALL TWISTY BLOATED, LIKE DIRTY OLD TOWEL WHEN YOUR TRYING TO WRING YOUR MOTHER'S BLOOD OUT OF IT IN A DISUSED CAR PARK.

SISTER CAROL IS YOUNGER THAN LOIS AND HAS HAD NINE HUSBANDS, EIGHT OF WHOM HAVE LEFT HER, AND HAD A BOY BY HER EIGHTH HUSBAND. A BIT LIKE A POWERLESS, PATHETIC, DIKEY KING HENRY VIIITH.

FACTFILE

AGE: 42
PLACE OF BIRTH:
NEWPORT, RHODE ISLAND
LOIS PEWTERSCHMIDT

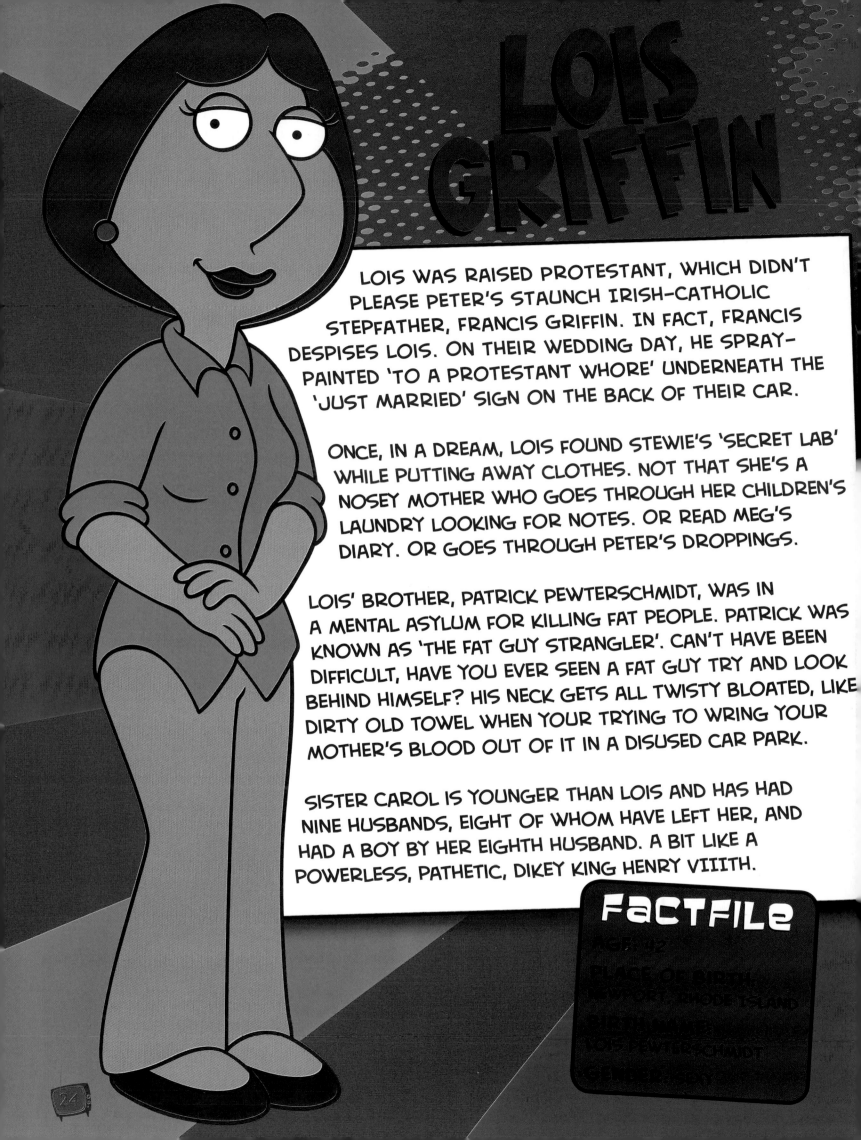

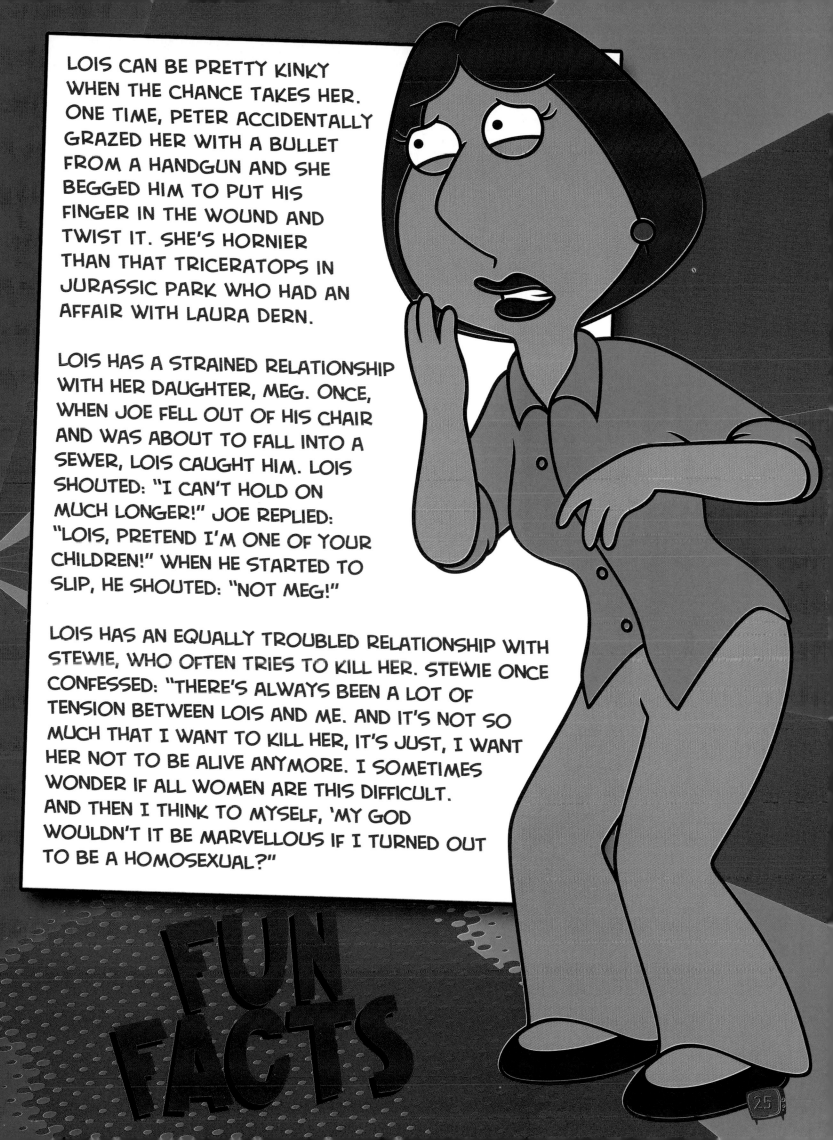

LOIS CAN BE PRETTY KINKY WHEN THE CHANCE TAKES HER. ONE TIME, PETER ACCIDENTALLY GRAZED HER WITH A BULLET FROM A HANDGUN AND SHE BEGGED HIM TO PUT HIS FINGER IN THE WOUND AND TWIST IT. SHE'S HORNIER THAN THAT TRICERATOPS IN JURASSIC PARK WHO HAD AN AFFAIR WITH LAURA DERN.

LOIS HAS A STRAINED RELATIONSHIP WITH HER DAUGHTER, MEG. ONCE, WHEN JOE FELL OUT OF HIS CHAIR AND WAS ABOUT TO FALL INTO A SEWER, LOIS CAUGHT HIM. LOIS SHOUTED: "I CAN'T HOLD ON MUCH LONGER!" JOE REPLIED: "LOIS, PRETEND I'M ONE OF YOUR CHILDREN!" WHEN HE STARTED TO SLIP, HE SHOUTED: "NOT MEG!"

LOIS HAS AN EQUALLY TROUBLED RELATIONSHIP WITH STEWIE, WHO OFTEN TRIES TO KILL HER. STEWIE ONCE CONFESSED: "THERE'S ALWAYS BEEN A LOT OF TENSION BETWEEN LOIS AND ME. AND IT'S NOT SO MUCH THAT I WANT TO KILL HER, IT'S JUST, I WANT HER NOT TO BE ALIVE ANYMORE. I SOMETIMES WONDER IF ALL WOMEN ARE THIS DIFFICULT. AND THEN I THINK TO MYSELF, 'MY GOD WOULDN'T IT BE MARVELLOUS IF I TURNED OUT TO BE A HOMOSEXUAL?"

FUN FACTS

MEET... LOIS GRIFFIN

LOIS GRIFFIN IS FAMILY GUY'S RANDY PIECE OF EYE CANDY AND PETER'S SEXUAL MODUS OPERANDI.

SHE'S USUALLY IN LOVE WITH HER HUSBAND EVEN ABANDONING A LIFETIME OF FINANCIAL WEALTH OFFERED TO HER BY HER FATHER CARTER PEWTERSCHMIDT TO MARRY THE MAN OF HER CHEESE-FUELLED DREAMS.

SHE OFFERS EQUALLY PATCHY SUCCOUR TO HER THREE CHILDREN. EVERY NOW AND THEN, HOWEVER, LOIS SHOWS THAT BENEATH HER STEELY VENEER LIES A PROUD, PROTECTIVE MOTHER.

LOIS GRIFFIN HAS AN ABSOLUTELY STUNNING BODY AND STUNNING BEAUTY – AND BOY, DOES SHE KNOW IT! BEFORE MEETING PETER, LOIS HAD RELATIONSHIPS WITH A LOT OF OTHER MEN AND RUMOUR IS THAT MARRIED LIFE HASN'T TAMED HER TOO MUCH.

WHEN LOIS SHOUTED SHOWTIME! EVEN THE MOST SEDATE MAN WOULD BE ABLE TO SEE THE LUST IN HER EYES. SHE COULD PROBABLY

HAVE HER PICK OF GUYS, BUT SHE STILL LOVES THE GENTLE AND TOLERANT PETER. OR SHOULD THAT BE SHE TOLERATES HIM?

SHE ADMIT THERE HAVE BEEN TIMES WHEN SHE'S FANCIED WALKING AWAY BUT SHE LOVES HER MAN... AND HIS DOG! SHE HAD A THING FOR GLENN QUAGMIRE BUT PETER WON HER OVER.

LIKE HER THREE CHILDREN, LOIS HAS NOT AGED FOR THE BEST PART OF A DECADE. AND SHE IS SO LOVING SHE DOESN'T EVEN REALISE HER YOUNGEST IS ALWAYS PLOTTING HER DOWNFALL.

THE LIFE AND TIMES OF LOIS GRIFFIN...

LOIS: OH, I HAVEN'T BEEN ON A COLLEGE CAMPUS IN YEARS. EVERYTHING SEEMS SO DIFFERENT.

STEWIE: REALLY? PERHAPS IF YOU LAID ON YOUR BACK WITH YOUR ANKLES BEHIND YOUR EARS THAT WOULD RING A FEW BELLS.

LOIS: HONEY, WHAT DO YOU SAY WE UH... CHRISTEN THESE NEW SHEETS, HUH?

PETER: WHY LOIS GRIFFIN, YOU NAUGHTY GIRL.

LOIS: HEHEHE... THAT'S ME.

PETER: YOU DIRTY HUSTLER.

LOIS: HEHEHEHE...

PETER: YOU FILTHY, STINKY PROSTITUTE.

LOIS: AHA, OK I GET IT...

PETER: YOU FOUL, VENEREAL DISEASE CARRYING, STREET WALKING WHORE.

LOIS: ALRIGHT, THAT'S ENOUGH!

BRAIN: UGH, I CAN'T BELIEVE YOU'RE SERVING A THREE-YEAR SENTENCE, IT SEEMS SO HARSH.

LOIS: WELL, THE ONLY UPSIDE IS THAT IT'S GIVEN ME TIME TO THINK ABOUT WHY I ENDED UP IN HERE. I GUESS I WAS STEALIN' BECAUSE I WAS SO SICK OF THE SAME OLD ROUTINE. I FELT LIKE I HAD A VOID IN MY LIFE, LIKE, LIKE, THERE WAS A SECRET HOLE IN ME...

QUAGMIRE: OH GOD!

LOIS: ...AND I WAS TRYIN' TO FILL THAT HOLE WITH ALL KINDS OF EXPENSIVE OBJECTS, AND THINGS...

QUAGMIRE: OH GOD!

LOIS: ...AND I FELT WONDERFUL WITH ALL THOSE THINGS FILLIN' THAT HOLE.

QUAGMIRE: OH GOD!!!

LOIS: I DID THIS TO MYSELF, SO I'M JUST GONNA HAVE TO LAY BACK AND LET THE PENAL SYSTEM TEACH ME A LESSON.

QUAGMIRE: THAT ONE IS ALSO SEXUAL.

LOIS: AND YOU KNOW WHAT? I'M GONNA TAKE THAT CHANCE MY FATHER NEVER LET ME TAKE WHEN I WAS YOUNGER. I'M GONNA BECOME A MODEL!

PETER: HEY, THAT'S FANTASTIC, LOIS! AND I'LL PLEASURE MYSELF TO YOUR PHOTOS.

CHRIS: ME TOO!

MEG: ME TOO!

PETER: OH! OH! GOD! MEG! THAT'S SICK! THAT'S YOUR MOTHER!

MEG: I'M JUST TRYING TO FIT IN.

PETER: GET OUT! GET OUT OF THIS HOUSE NOW! (MEG LEAVES).

PETER: THAT'S A GOOD ABOUT YOUR MODELLING, LOIS.

LOIS GRIFFIN: COME ON STEWIE, DON'T BE AFRAID. IT'S JUST WATER, IT'S NOT GONNA BITE.

STEWIE GRIFFIN: SHUT UP! I KNOW IT'S NOT GOING TO BITE, STUPID! WHAT A STUPID THING TO SAY. YOU DROWN IN IT YOU MORON! IT DOESN'T HAVE TO BITE YOU!

LOIS: WHAT'S GOING ON DOWN HERE?

STEWIE: OH, WE'RE PLAYING HOUSE.

LOIS: THAT BOY'S ALL TIED UP.

STEWIE: ROMAN POLANSKI'S HOUSE.

LOIS: I CARE ABOUT THE SIZE OF YOUR PENIS AS MUCH AS YOU CARE ABOUT THE SIZE OF MY BREASTS.

PETER: OH MY GOD! (RUNS OFF CRYING).

PETER: LOIS, I CAN'T FIND MY FAVOURITE PAIR OF UNDERWEAR.

LOIS: WHICH ONE? THE ONE WHERE YOU RIPPED HOLE IN IT FROM WHEN YOU GOT STUCK IN THAT AIRPLANE BATHROOM FROM WHEN YOU GOT THE TROTS?

PETER: NO, I'M LOOKING FOR THE PAIR FROM WHEN I HAD TO HOLD IT IN BECAUSE IT WAS THAT EXTRA LONG PALM SUNDAY SERVICE AND I THOUGHT BLOWING GAS WOULD OFFEND GOD SO I LET IT RIP IN THE VESTIBULE AFTER SERVICE.

LOIS: TOP DRAWER.

LOIS: OH, LOOK, MEG, IT'S YOUR LITTLE BABY BOOTIES. OH, AND YOUR LITTLE BRONZE HAT. AND YOUR TAIL.

MEG: MY WHAT?

LOIS: NOTHING.

PETER: WE ALL KNOW THAT NO WOMEN ANYWHERE WANTS TO HAVE SEX WITH ANYONE AND TO TITILLATE US WITH ANY THOUGHTS OTHERWISE IS JUST BOGUS.

LOIS: AH, HE IS SO RIGHT ON. WOMEN ARE SUCH TEASES. THAT'S WHY I WENT BACK TO MEN.

MY DAYS IN COLLEGE WERE SO EXCITING. THIS ONE TIME, THE NATIONAL GUARD CAME AND SHOT SOME OF MY FRIENDS.

LOIS: A GOOD BREAKFAST IS THE FOUNDATION OF A GOOD DAY.

BRIAN: AND A BAD BREAKFAST IS THE FOUNDATION OF INDIGESTION!

LOIS: KIDS, YOUR GRANDFATHER'S EARS ARE NOT GROSS AND THEY ARE CERTAINLY NOT AN ENCHANTED FOREST.

29

WHERE THEY LIVE: SPOONER STREET

SPOONER STREET IS LOCATED TO THE WEST OF DOWNTOWN QUAHOG. IT IS HOME TO THE MOST ENERGETIC, VIBRANT AND CRIMINALLY VIOLENT BUNCH OF FUN-LOVIN' NE'ER-DO-WELLS IN THE WHOLE OF ANIMATEDTVLAND.

THE STREET HAS ALREADY EARNED SOME INCREDIBLE ACCOLADES, INCLUDING, IN 'LOVE THY TROPHY', A PRIZE FOR THEIR WHO'S THE BOSS-THEMED FLOAT. THAT COMMUNITY PARADE FLOAT COMPETITION DIDN'T KNOW WHAT HAD HIT IT, A BIT LIKE TONY DANZA WHEN HE REALISED HE HADN'T MADE IT TO THE FINAL CASTING ON SUPER MARIO BROTHERS. HE LOST OUT TO BOB HOSKINS, MAN. BOB HOSKINS! HE'S ABOUT AS ITALIAN AS BRAVERY.

THEY'RE CRAZY AND THEY'RE KOOKY, MYSTERIOUS AND KOOKY AND LIVE ON SPOONER STREET.

27

MORBIDLY OBESE ALBERT IS DIAGNOSED WITH DIABETES BUT WOULD STILL SWAP ONE OF HIS LIMBS FOR A PIECE OF DELICIOUS CHOCOLATE.

29

LOVEABLE SEXUAL DEVIANT GLENN QUAGMIRE, AND FORMERLY JOAN QUAGMIRE, LIVES JUST A STONE'S THROW FROM THE GRIFFINS AT 29. JOAN USED TO LIVE WITH HER HUSBAND UNTIL SHE THREW HERSELF IN FRONT OF DEATH AT GLENN'S FAKE FUNERAL. IT'S A LONGER STORY THAN THAT - GO SEE "I TAKE THEE QUAGMIRE" SO WE CAN SAVE SOME INK. QUAGMIRE NOW LIVES WITH A GAGGLE OF ASIAN GIRLS, ALL OF WHOM ARE TAGGED. GIGGITY.

30 THE BROWNS. CLEVELAND BROWN, FORMERLY JOINED BY LORETTA AND CLEVELAND, JR., LIVE AT NUMBER 30. LORETTA LEFT AFTER THE FAMOUS 'QUAGMIRE AFFAIR'. IN PETARDED, MEG, CHRIS, AND STEWIE ALSO STAYED AT CLEVELAND'S BRIEFLY WHEN THEY WERE TAKEN AWAY FROM PETER. CLEVELAND IS SO BIG HE HAS EVEN GOTTEN HIS OWN SHOW, A BIT LIKE WHEN JOEY FROM FRIENDS GOT HIS OWN SHOW, BUT FUNNY.

31 IF YOU'RE WONDERING WHY THE GRIFFIN'S HOUSE IS IN BLACK, THAT'S BECAUSE IT WAS TEMPORARILY DISCOVERED TO BE OUTSIDE OF THE UNITED STATES. OH, HOW WE MISS THE WARMING EMBRACE AND HIDDEN FONDLING OF PETORIA, THE LAND OF THE FRAYED AND HOME OF THE BRIE. THE MICRO NATION OF PETORIA WAS A LAND WHERE A MAN COULD SING A PARODY OF 'U CAN'T TOUCH THIS' ENTITLED 'CAN'T TOUCH ME' WITHOUT FEAR OF BEING SUED BY MC HAMMER. A GREAT LAND.

33 THE SWANSONS. JOE, BONNIE AND SUSIE SWANSON LIVE AT NUMBER 33. THEIR SON, KEVIN SWANSON, WAS KILLED IN IRAQ. THE EXACT CAUSE OF HIS DEATH REMAINS A MYSTERY. WE THINK IT MAY HAVE BEEN AN IRATE, IRRATIONAL AND IRASCIBLE DEATH BECAUSE, AS YOU KNOW, ALL WORDS IN IRAQ BEGIN WITH 'IR'. THAT'S HOW LOYAL THEY ARE AMERICA. WE COULD LEARN. WE COULD LEARN.

89 STANFORD CORDRAY USED TO LIVE AT 89 SPOONER STREET BEFORE MOVING TO ASPEN, COLORADO. STEWIE MISTAKENLY SOLD HIM RUPERT, HE MOVED TO COLORADO, STEWIE CHASED HIM DOWN, CHALLENGED HIM TO A SKI CONTEST TO WIN RUPERT BACK AND LOST, BUT THEN WON. KINDA.

90 POPULAR PAEDOPHILE HERBERT AND HIS ASS-DRAGGIN' DOG JESSE LIVE DOWN THE STREET. JUST FAR ENOUGH FOR THE CHILDREN OF SPOONER STREET TO SLEEP PEACEFULLY AT NIGHT, WITHOUT MORPHINE.

? KYLE, THE BULLY, AND HIS PARENTS ARE ALSO NEIGHBOURS OF THE GRIFFINS BUT NO-ONE KNOWS WHERE. AN INCOGNITO BULLY - TERRIFYING, BUT EXCITING!

MEG

PROFILE & GRIFFIN INTERVIEW

I'M JUST TRYING TO FIT IN!

MEG GRIFFIN

MEG IS MORE OR LESS DESPISED BY EVERYONE WHO KNOWS HER. SOME PEOPLE ARE APATHETIC, BUT THAT'S AS POSITIVE AS THEY FEEL. CLEVELAND HAS OPENLY ADMITTED TO PETER: "MEG IS MY LEAST FAVOURITE OF YOUR CHILDREN."

EVERYONE WANTS TO BE PART OF THE COOL CROWD, BUT NO-ONE MORE THAN MEG. LIKE A POLICEMAN AT A SOCIAL GATHERING, SHE'LL DO JUST ABOUT ANYTHING TO FIT IN.

GO LOOK UP MEG'S FAMILY TREE AND YOU'LL FIND A CROOKED BRANCH: ACCORDING TO BRIAN, PETER IS NOT HER REAL FATHER. PETER, WHILE ATTEMPTING TO PERSUADE A COURT THAT BRIAN SHOULD HAVE ACCESS TO HIS PUPPIES, OBSERVED THAT IF HE WERE HALF THE DAD THAT BRIAN IS HE WOULD KNOW CERTAIN FACTS ABOUT HIS CHILDREN, INCLUDING THE FACT THAT 'MEG'S REAL FATHER IS ....' BRIAN ANSWERED "STAN THOMSON". THE IRONY IS THAT MEG WAS LISTENING TO MUSIC ON HEADPHONES AT THE TIME AND MISSED THE REVELATION.

FACTFILE

AGE: 17

PLACE OF BIRTH: QUAHOG, RHODE ISLAND

BIRTH NAME: MEGAN GRIFFIN

GENDER: GIRLBOYGIRL

34

WHEN LOIS AND MEG WERE ON SPRING BREAK TOGETHER, HER MOTHER LOVINGLY TOLD HER DAUGHTER THAT SHE WAS BORN WHEN BIRTH CONTROL FAILED DUE TO TAKING ANTIBIOTICS.

MEG HAS BEEN VOICED BY FIVE DIFFERENT PEOPLE. RACHAEL MACFARLANE, THE YOUNGER SISTER OF SETH, DID THE PILOT; LACEY CHABERT, WHO STARS AS CLAUDIA SALINGER IN 'PARTY OF FIVE', DID THE FIRST SEASON; MILA KUNIS, WHO IS MARRIED TO 'HOME ALONE'S' MACAULAY CAULKIN, IS THE CURRENT VOICE AND TARA STRONG, WHO DYES HER HAIR BLONDE, PROVIDES THE SINGING VOICE. JOHN VIENER DID THE VOICE WHEN SHE WAS 'RON' IN STU & STEWIE'S EXCELLENT ADVENTURE.

MEG WAS ORIGINALLY A SWEET DAUGHTER WHO, KINDA COMEDICALLY SPEAKIN', TOOK THE BLAME FOR THE TERRIBLE THINGS DONE BY HER FELLOW FAMILY MEMBERS. BUT OVER THE YEARS, FAMILY GUY WRITERS DIDN'T HAVE THE WIT OR IMAGINATION FOR THAT, SO THEY MADE HER DESPERATE AND PATHETIC.

FUN FACTS

35

MEET... MEG GRIFFIN

MEG IS MUCH PLAINER IN REAL LIFE THAN ON THE SHOW. BUT SHE HAS ADMIRERS – INCLUDING QUAGMIRE AND BRIAN.

MEG HAS HAD A FEW RELATIONSHIPS BUT THERE HAVE ALSO BEEN SOME PRETTY HORRIBLE REJECTIONS. MEN JUST DON'T STICK AROUND HER FOR LONG.

SHE'S HATED BY HER FAMILY BUT AT LEAST SHE KNOWS IT! THEY DO PAY HER A LOT OF ATTENTION THOUGH... MOST OF IT BAD! LIKE ANY GIRL SHE HAS DREAMS BUT SADLY MOST OF MEG'S END UP BEING NIGHTMARES IN REAL LIFE.

YOU WILL MOSTLY SEE HER WEARING A BEANIE-LIKE HAT AND GLASSES WITH A PINK AND WHITE SHIRT, BLUE JEANS AND CLOGS. SHE APPEARS FAT AND IS OFTEN MISTAKEN FOR A BOY.

POOR OLD MEG. SHE'S NOT POPULAR. SHE'S NOT GOOD LOOKING. BUT AT LEAST SHE IS A TRIER HOPING FOR POPULARITY AND ACCEPTANCE AT SCHOOL. AND THE WORLD LOVES A TRIER... DOESN'T IT?

THE LIFE AND TIMES OF MEG GRIFFIN

MEG: I JUST WANT TO KILL MYSELF I'M GONNA GO UPSTAIRS AND EAT A WHOLE BOWL OF PEANUTS. I'M ALLERGIC TO PEANUTS. YOU DON'T KNOW ANYTHING ABOUT ME.

PETER: WHO WAS THAT GUY?

MEG: LOOK MOM I'VE HAD IT. I'M NOT BABYSITTING ANYMORE. IT'S SATURDAY NIGHT I COULD BE OUT HAVING A LIFE.

LOIS: MEG, IF YOU DON'T WANNA BABYSIT ANYMORE THAT'S FINE, BUT DON'T YOU STAND THERE AND LIE TO ME.

PETER: OH, HO MEG, SHE TORCHED YOUR ASS MAN! SHE TORCHED YOUR ASS.

MEG: PLEASE GO OUT WITH ME. I'M JUST TRYING TO MAKE NEIL JEALOUS. I PROMISE I'LL PAY AND EVERYTHING.

BOY: THAT SOUNDS COOL BUT I'M GONNA BE IN THE HOSPITAL THAT NIGHT (SHOOTS HIMSELF WITH A NAIL GUN).

LOIS: DEAR DIARY, KEVIN IS SO HOT. TODAY HE WAS RAKING THE YARD. GOD I WISH HE'D THROW ME INTO THAT PILE OF LEAVES.

MEG: HEY WHAT'S EVERYONE... OH MY GOD! YOU'RE READING MY DIARY! I HATE YOU ALL (RUNS AWAY CRYING)

PETER: KEEP GOING!

MEG: WOW! THIS LOOKS JUST LIKE MY ROOM AT HOME!

LOIS: YEAH! EXCEPT FOR ALL OF THE TROPHIES AND PICTURES OF FRIENDS.

MEG: LOOK EVERYBODY I GOT A MAKEOVER!!

PETER: AW, MEG I THOUGHT YOU WERE ALWAYS BEAUTIFUL... (BURSTS OUT LAUGHING). WHOA, COULDN'T DO THAT WITH A STRAIGHT FACE, HUH? CHRIS, GO BURN ALL OF MEG'S OLD PICTURES.

MEG: DAD, IF I DON'T GET MY DRIVER'S LICENCE, I'LL NEVER HAVE ANY BOYFRIENDS, I'LL NEVER GET MARRIED AND I'LL HAVE TO ADOPT A KID LIKE ROSIE O'DONNELL.

PETER: MEG... ARE YOU IMPLYING THAT ROSIE O'DONNELL CAN'T DRIVE?

LOIS: OH, WHAT ABOUT THIS, MEG? A PINK BABY-TEE THAT SAYS "LITTLE SLUT." THAT SEEMS PRETTY HIP.

MEG: I DON'T KNOW IF THAT'S REALLY ME, MOM.

LOIS: WELL, THEY'VE GOT ONE THAT SAYS "PORN STAR" AND ANOTHER THAT SAYS "SPERM DUMPSTER." AND THEY'RE ALL WRITTEN IN GLITTER.

MEG: ALL RIGHT. GIVE ME "SPERM DUMPSTER."

BRIAN: HEY DOC, WHAT THE HELL ARE YOU DOING HERE?

DOCTOR: YOUR FAMILY HAS SOMETHING TO SAY.

MEG: (READING FROM A PIECE OF PAPER) BRIAN, I KNOW I DON'T SPEAK UP MUCH, AND IT'S REALLY HARD FOR ME TO TALK ABOUT MY FEELINGS, BUT...

DOCTOR: WHY DON'T WE START WITH SOMEONE MORE INTERESTING? PETER?

MEG: I LIKE HIM, HE REMEMBERS MY NAME!

MEG: OH MY GOD, WE'RE GONNA DIE! THERE'S SO MUCH OF LIFE I HAVEN'T EXPERIENCED. I NEVER EVEN GOT THE CHANCE TO BE SOME DRUNK COLLEGE GUY'S LAST RESORT.

WHAT DO YOU KNOW?

QUESTION 1

Patrick Pewterschmidt, Lois's brother who was in a mental asylum for killing fat people, was voiced by which superhero?

QUESTION 2

What is the name of Brian's father who may or may not be racist, depending on which side of the white picket fence you sit?

QUESTION 3

Which intergalactic honey provides the voice for my sexy lesbian boss at Pawtucket Brewery, Angela?

QUESTION 4

This is a doozy: what was the name of the guy that beat me at Shploopel?

QUESTION 5

Who is the Grand Master of the Skull and Bones Society?

QUESTION 6

What is the name of the gravely voiced old sailor whose father was a tree?

QUESTION 7

What was the name of that English prick Nigel Pinchley's daughter who Stewie almost made talk proper?

QUESTION 8

Who is that bitch Alexis Radcliffe?

QUESTION 9

What is the name of the Native American Indian bathroom attendant at Geronimo's Palace Casino.

SO, YOU'RE A WISE GUY, HUH? A BIG, TOUGH WISE GUY? A BIG, TOUGH WISE GUY WHO, WHEN HIS MOTHER GOES TO BINGO, SECRETLY SINGS 'CABARET' WHILE WEARING THE CONTENTS OF HER WARDROBE, HER FRUIT BOWL AND THOSE SIZE 11 HIGH HEELS BOUGHT FROM THE SHOP WITH THE PAINTED WINDOWS.

WELL, IF YOU'RE SUCH A BIG CLEVER HOMME, WHY, IF EVOLUTION IS A FACT, DO MONKEYS STILL EXIST? NOT SO CLEVER NOW, HUH? I'LL TELL YOU. IT'S BECAUSE MARK WAHLBERG CAME BACK. THAT'S WHY. GOD DAMN YOU ALL. ANSWER ME THIS, THESE, THISES...

QUESTION 10

Who is Mayor Adam West married to?

QUESTION 11

In 'Ocean's Three and Half', which potty mouth is going to owe the swear jar a fortune?

QUESTION 12

In 'Family Gay' with whose gene does Peter get injected shortly before being injected with the gay gene?

QUESTION 13

In 'The Juice Is Loose' who does a three minute segment that no-one liked?

QUESTION 14

In 'FOX-y Lady' it is revealed Rush Limbaugh is actually a disguise worn by which fat film fatty fat?

QUESTION 15

In 'Not All Dogs Go To Heaven' it is revealed that Mayor Adam West lives with which hockey player?

QUESTION 16

In '420' the ratings for which TV programme goes through the roof when marijuana is legalised?

QUESTION 17

In the 'Stand By Me' segment of 'Three Kings' who is in Mayor West's gang alongside Beast-Man and Mer-Man?

QUESTION 18

In 'I Dream of Jesus', in whose apartment is Jesus found face down and unconscious?

QUESTION 19

Who is Quagmire dressed as in the party at the beginning of 'Love Blactually'?

QUESTION 20

Who, along with Brian and Stewie, flees from the Nazis in 'Road To Germany'?

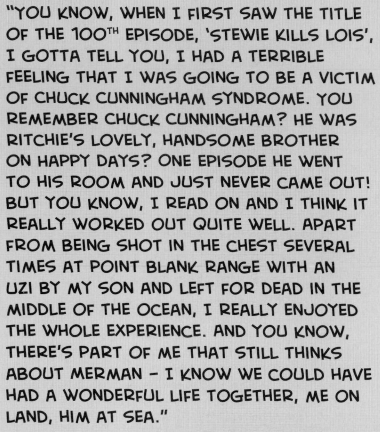

"YOU KNOW, WHEN I FIRST SAW THE TITLE OF THE 100TH EPISODE, 'STEWIE KILLS LOIS', I GOTTA TELL YOU, I HAD A TERRIBLE FEELING THAT I WAS GOING TO BE A VICTIM OF CHUCK CUNNINGHAM SYNDROME. YOU REMEMBER CHUCK CUNNINGHAM? HE WAS RITCHIE'S LOVELY, HANDSOME BROTHER ON HAPPY DAYS? ONE EPISODE HE WENT TO HIS ROOM AND JUST NEVER CAME OUT! BUT YOU KNOW, I READ ON AND I THINK IT REALLY WORKED OUT QUITE WELL. APART FROM BEING SHOT IN THE CHEST SEVERAL TIMES AT POINT BLANK RANGE WITH AN UZI BY MY SON AND LEFT FOR DEAD IN THE MIDDLE OF THE OCEAN, I REALLY ENJOYED THE WHOLE EXPERIENCE. AND YOU KNOW, THERE'S PART OF ME THAT STILL THINKS ABOUT MERMAN – I KNOW WE COULD HAVE HAD A WONDERFUL LIFE TOGETHER, ME ON LAND, HIM AT SEA."

100TH EPISODE

"HEY MOM, WHAT ABOUT THE BIRTHDAY PRESENTS? YOU HAVEN'T MENTIONED THE SMOKER'S TOOTHPOLISH, WHICH I SEE YOU STILL HAVEN'T USED."

"OR THE CAN'T SLOW DOWN. YOU KNOW, LIONEL RITCHIE WENT THROUGH A LOT OF PERSONAL HURT AND BARED HIS SOUL TO BRING YOU THAT ALBUM, LOIS. I THINK YOU SHOULD BE A LITTLE MORE RESPECTFUL TO THE MAN PEOPLE DESCRIBE AS THE WHITE STEVIE WONDER."

"YOU PEOPLE MAKE ME SMILE INSIDE. THE READERS AREN'T INTERESTED IN YOUR PETTY SQUABBLES OVER NARRATIVE; THEY ARE FASCINATED BY OUR CHARACTERS' INTERNAL DIALOGUE, THEIR MOTIVATION. STEWIE IS A SANE BABY IN A MAD, MAD WORLD. HE IS DRIVEN TO DISTRACTION BY, AND I QUOTE: 'ALL THE INDIGNITIES HE HAS HAD TO SUFFER DAY IN AND DAY OUT AFTER YEARS OF MATRIARCHAL TYRANNY.' I KNOW THERE'S A LOT OF STEWIE FANS OUT THERE WHO WERE ROOTING FOR THE LITTLE GUY."

"I THINK WE ALL KNOW MY PART WAS UNDERWRITTEN. I MEAN, I WAS RELEGATED TO THE ROLE OF A DOGSBODY. IF EVER THE WRITING WAS ON THE WALL."

"UNDERWRITTEN? TRY BEING CALLED AN ABORTION SURVIVOR."

"HEY, COME ON MEG, YOU HAD THAT WHOLE SEGUE WAY ABOUT SCREWING THE NEW YORK KNICKS. I WILL NEVER TOUCH ANOTHER PACKET OF HOT DOGS. ON THAT, DO YOU THINK THAT COULD BE CLASSED AS CANNIBALISM?"

"I GOTTA SPEAK TO MY AGENT."

"OF ALL THE EPISODES ASIDE, I THINK ANY SENTIENT BEING WOULD CLASS THE RINGO STARR SONG-WRITING GAG AT THE TOP. THAT GUY MAKES PAULA ABDUL LOOK TALENTED."

"COME ON STEWIE, RINGO WAS ONE OF THE WORLD'S GREATEST DRUMMERS IN ONE OF THE WORLD'S GREATEST BANDS."

"OK, SO PAUL MCCARTNEY ONCE DESCRIBED HIM AS THE BEST DRUMMER IN THE WORLD. IT DOESN'T MEAN IT'S TRUE."

"I LIKE TO THINK THE 100TH EPISODE IS METAPHORICAL. LET'S JUST HOPE AN EPISODE ABOUT COMING BACK FROM THE DEAD TO AVENGE WRONGDOING SENDS A MESSAGE OUT TO THOSE WISE-ASSES WHO CANCELLED US FOR TWO AND HALF FREAKIN' YEARS BEFORE WE CAME BACK FROM THE DEAD TO BE DESPISED BY EVERYONE GOOD AND DECENT IN WESTERN CIVILISATION."

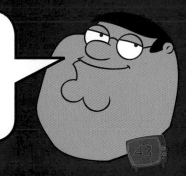

STEWIE GRIFFIN

STEWIE IS FIERCELY PROUD OF HIS DEATH COUNT. HE HAS KILLED A CULT LEADER IN 'CHITTY CHITTY DEATH BANG', HIS NEAR FUTURE SELF AND CHRIS' FUTURE WIFE VANESSA IN 'STEWIE GRIFFIN: THE UNTOLD STORY', VERN AND JOHNNY IN 'SAVING PRIVATE BRIAN' AND OLIVIA FULLER AND VICTOR IN 'CHICK CANCER'. IMPRESSIVE.

THE ONLY OTHER PERSON WHO HAS EVER REALLY UNDERSTOOD WHAT STEWIE SAYS IS BRIAN'S GIRLFRIEND, JILLIAN. IN 'STEWIE KILLS LOIS' AND 'LOIS KILLS STEWIE' HE IS BRIEFLY UNDERSTOOD BY THE GRIFFINS, BUT THAT'S IT. THE REST OF IT IS JUST 'GA GA GOO GOO' AND FART SOUNDS.

EVEN THOUGH HE'S A GENIUS, IF YOU PLAY PEEK-A-BOO WITH HIM, HE'LL THINK YOU'VE DISAPPEARED.

WORLD DOMINATION. THAT'S IT. STEWIE'S ULTIMATE GOAL AND HE WON'T LET ANYONE OR ANY THING OR ANYONE STOP HIM. BUT TAKE HIS BLANKY AND WATCH HIM WAIL.

INVENTIONS. STEWIE'S FIRST INVENTION WAS A MIND CONTROL DEVICE WHICH, IN FAMILY GUY'S FIRST EPISODE, HE USED ON A JUDGE TO SAVE PETER FROM JAIL. IF YOU POINTED A MIND CONTROL DEVICE AT PETER, WOULD IT EXPLODE?

ENJOYING PAIN IS SOMETHING STEWIE AND HIS ARCH-ENEMY LOIS MAY WELL HAVE IN COMMON. ONCE, WHEN LOIS SPANKED STEWIE FOR BREAKING HER PEARL NECKLACE, HE REPEATEDLY TRIED TO PROVOKE HER INTO REPEATING THE SPANKING. HE'S A NAUGHTY, NAUGHTY BOY.

FACTFILE

AGE: 1 (EIGHT SEASONS)

PLACE OF BIRTH: QUAHOG, RHODE ISLAND

BIRTH NAME: STEWART GILLIGAN GRIFFIN

GENDER: BABY

STEWIE'S E-MAIL ADDRESS IS LOISMUSTDIE@YAHOO.COM

AN INFLATABLE STEWIE RECENTLY STARRED IN A COCA COLA COMMERCIAL ALONGSIDE CHARLIE BROWN. HEY FAMILY GUY, WHAT HAPPENED TO BEING THE CULTURAL MOUTHPIECE OF ANTI-CORPORATE AMERICA? WHAT? YOU NEVER WERE? OH, THAT'S OKAY THEN. SELL OUT ALL YOU CAN.

STEWIE AND BRIAN WERE ONCE SIAMESE TWINS, LIKE THE OLSEN SKELETONS.

FUN FACTS

MEET... STEWIE GRIFFIN

STEWIE GRIFFIN IS A LITTLE MAN IN A BIG RUSH. AGITATED AND OFTEN VERY DISTANT, HE ALSO HAS A LOT OF PENT UP AGGRESSION.

THIS ONE-YEAR-OLD LOVES TO WORK IN HIS LABORATORY OR INVENT THINGS LIKE ADVANCED FIGHTER-JETS, WEATHER CONTROL, ROBOTS, A TIME MACHINE, A SHRINKING POD OR A TELEPORTATION DEVICE. ALL USEFUL ITEMS IN HIS BID FOR WORLD DOMINATION.

RUMOURS ABOUT HIS SEXUALITY WERE STIRRED BY THE EPISODE 'STEWIE: THE UNTOLD STORY' WHICH FLASHED FORWARD TO SHOW HIM AS A 35-YEAR-OLD VIRGIN. THE YOUNGEST GRIFFIN HAS HOWEVER BEEN ROMANTICALLY LINKED WITH SUSIE SWANSON.

USE OF THE TOILET IS STILL ALIEN TO HIM. HE TALKS TO HIS TEDDY BEAR, RUPERT, AND HIS MOTHER IS NOT THE MOST POPULAR PERSON IN HIS LIFE. OK, LET'S BE HONEST, HE WOULD LIKE TO KILL HER!

THE LIFE AND TIMES OF STEWIE GRIFFIN

STEWIE: IT WASN'T EVEN ABOUT THE EGGS, REALLY. FRANKLY, I LIKE THE YOLKS. I HAVE NO PROBLEM. THERE'S ALWAYS BEEN A LOT OF TENSION BETWEEN LOIS AND ME. AND IT'S NOT SO MUCH THAT I WANT TO KILL HER, IT'S JUST, I WANT HER NOT TO BE ALIVE ANYMORE. I SOMETIMES WONDER IF ALL WOMEN ARE THIS DIFFICULT. AND THEN I THINK TO MYSELF, 'MY GOD WOULDN'T IT BE MARVELLOUS IF I TURNED OUT TO BE A HOMOSEXUAL?'

LOIS: (FINDS NOTE IN STEWIE'S POCKET) HUH, WHAT'S THIS? YOU KNOW STEWIE, MOMMY DOESN'T USUALLY READ THINGS OUT OF CHRIS'S POCKET. SHE'S MORE RESPECTFUL THAN THAT.

STEWIE: WHATEVER HELPS YOU SLEEP AT NIGHT, BITCH.

STEWIE: (WHEN BRIAN FINDS HIS MOTHER STUFFED): "SOMEONE MUST HAVE SAID SOMETHING FUNNY, BECAUSE YOUR MOTHER'S IN STITCHES!"

BRIAN: YOU'RE DRUNK.

STEWIE: YOU'RE SEXY.

STEWIE: DID YOU HEAR THAT MEG? GUYS CAN MARRY OTHER GUYS NOW. SO...THIS IS AWKWARD, BUT I MEAN, IF THEY CAN DO THAT, THAT IS PRETTY MUCH IT FOR YOU, ISN'T IT? I MEAN YOU AS WELL PACK IT IN. GAME OVER.

STEWIE: UH YOU'VE REACHED STEWIE AND BRIAN, WE'RE NOT HERE RIGHT NOW, UH AND IF THIS IS MOM, UH SEND MONEY BECAUSE WE'RE COLLEGE STUDENTS AND WE NEED MONEY FOR BOOKS... AND HIGHLIGHTERS...AND.... RAMEN NOODLES...AND CONDOMS, FOR SEXUAL RELATIONS WITH OUR CLASSMATES.

OLIVIA: YOU ARE THE WEAKEST LINK, GOODBYE.

STEWIE: OH GOSH THAT'S FUNNY! THAT'S REALLY FUNNY! DO YOU WRITE YOUR OWN MATERIAL? DO YOU? BECAUSE THAT IS SO FRESH. YOU ARE THE WEAKEST LINK GOODBYE. YOU KNOW, I'VE NEVER HEARD ANYONE MAKE THAT JOKE BEFORE. HMM. YOU'RE THE FIRST. I'VE NEVER HEARD ANYONE REFERENCE, REFERENCE THAT OUTSIDE THE PROGRAMME BEFORE. BECAUSE THAT'S WHAT SHE SAYS ON THE SHOW RIGHT? ISN'T IT? YOU ARE THE WEAKEST LINK GOODBYE. AND, AND YET YOU'VE TAKEN THAT AND

USED IT OUT OF CONTEXT TO INSULT ME IN THIS EVERYDAY SITUATION. GOD WHAT A CLEVER, SMART GIRL YOU MUST BE, TO COME UP WITH A JOKE LIKE THAT ALL BY YOURSELF. ANY TITANIC JOKES YOU WANT TO THROW AT ME TOO?

MEG: EVERYBODY! GUESS WHAT I AM?

STEWIE: HMM, THE END RESULT OF A DRUNKEN BACK SEAT GROPE-FEST AND A BROKEN PROPHYLACTIC?

BUTLER: YOUR EGGS ARE CUT SIR.

STEWIE: CUT MY MILK!

BUTLER: I CAN'T SIR, IT'S LIQUID.

STEWIE: IMBECILE! FREEZE IT, THEN CUT IT, AND IF YOU QUESTION ME AGAIN I'LL PUT YOU ON DIAPER DETAIL AND I PROMISE I WON'T MAKE IT EASY FOR YOU.

STEWIE: I WANT PANCAKES!! YOU PEOPLE UNDERSTAND EVERY LANGUAGE EXCEPT ENGLISH! YO QUIERO PANCAKES! DONNEZ-MOI PANCAKES! CLICK-CLICK-BLOODY-CLICK PANCAKES!

LOIS: WHAT KIND OF EGOTISTICAL, SELFISH, MORONIC AND IDIOTIC PERSON WOULD GET LIPOSUCTION... WHO? WHO? (PETER WALKS IN AT HALF OF HIS WEIGHT)

STEWIE: OH MY GOD... IT HAS FINALLY HAPPENED, HE HAS BECOME SO MASSIVE THAT HE COLLAPSED INTO HIMSELF LIKE A NEUTRON STAR.

STEWIE: HEY LOOK! THE FAT ONE MADE A FUNNY! OKAY, I GOT ONE. IF YOU WERE TO COOK ANY SLOWER, WHY YOU WOULDN'T BE COOKING VERY FAST NOW WOULD YOU? WELL THAT WASN'T VERY FUNNY. OKAY, IF YOU WERE TO COOK ANY SLOWER, YOU WOULDN'T NEED AN EGG TIMER, YOU WOULD NEED AN EGG CALENDAR.

STEWIE: WHAT THE HELL IS THIS? I SAID EGG WHITES ONLY! ARE YOU TRYING TO GIVE ME A BLOODY HEART ATTACK? MAKE IT AGAIN!

STEWIE: EXCELLENT, THE MIND CONTROL DEVICE IS NEARING COMPLETION!

LOIS: STEWIE, NO TOYS AT THE TABLE.

STEWIE: DAMN YOU VILE WOMAN! YOU'VE IMPEDED MY WORK SINCE THE DAY I ESCAPED FROM YOUR WRETCHED WOMB.

LOIS: DON'T POUT NOW SWEETIE, WHEN YOU WERE BORN THE DOCTOR TOLD US YOU WERE THE HAPPIEST NEWBORN HE'D EVER DELIVERED.

STEWIE: OF COURSE. THAT WAS MY VICTORY DAY! THE FRUITION OF MY DEEPLY LAID PLANS TO ESCAPE FROM THAT CURSED OVARIAN BASTILLE! RETURN THE DEVICE WOMAN!

LOIS: NO TOYS, STEWIE.

STEWIE: VERY WELL THEN. BUT MARK MY WORDS, WHEN YOU LEAST EXPECT IT, YOUR UPPANCE SHALL COME.

SupernaTuRaL CHaRaCTeRs

"IT'S CLOSE TO MIDNIGHT AND SOMETHING EVIL'S LURKING IN THE DARK. UNDER THE MOONLIGHT, YOU SEE A SIGHT THAT ALMOST STOPS YOUR HEART. YOU TRY TO SCREAM BUT TERROR TAKES THE SOUND BEFORE YOU MAKE IT. YOU START TO FREEZE AS HORROR LOOKS YOU RIGHT BETWEEN THE EYES. YOU'RE PARALYZED... 'CAUSE THROUGH THE JACK DANIELS INDUCED HAZE YOU CAN SEE JOAN RIVERS SQUIRMING ORGASMICALLY BENEATH YOU." THE REGULAR FAMILY GUY UNIVERSE MAY BE POPULATED BY MORE FREAKS THAN FREAKSVILLE BUT THERE IS ANOTHER WORLD THAT LURKS IN THE SHADOWS, NO, NOT THE WIVES OF THE NRA, THE WORLD OF JESUS, GOD, SATAN AND DEATH. (DID YOU KNOW THAT ALL FOUR OF THOSE GUYS CHARGE AN ABSOLUTE FORTUNE FOR APPEARANCES – JERRY BRUCKHEIMER IS THEIR AGENT – WHAT YA' GONNA DO?)

YOU WANT TO KNOW JESUS? YOU WANT TO KNOW THE MAN? EASY, TAKE JIM CAVIEZEL'S WAY, DAVID COPPERFIELD'S TRUTH AND GENE KELLY'S LIGHT AND YOU'RE RIGHT THERE BASKING IN HIS HEAVENLY GLOW. YOU KNOW IT'S RUMOURED THAT HIS POWERS MAY

HAVE BEEN EXAGGERATED; HE WAS REALLY JUST A GOOD SONG AND DANCE MAN BUT THERE'S NOTHING WRONG WITH THAT: MICHAEL JACKSON TOUCHED PEOPLE TOO. IT'S ALSO RUMOURED THAT JESUS' SON OF GOD DELUSIONS WERE BECAUSE HE HAS LITTLE MAN SYNDROME, WHICH EXPLAINS WHY DANNY DE VITO ENDS EVER ARGUMENT BY YELLING 'I'LL TELL MY BROTHER ARNOLD SCHWARZENEGGER YOU SAID THAT!' WE ALSO KNOW JESUS COMES TO LIVE ON EARTH FOR A VERY SHORT TIME EVERY COUPLE OF YEARS, LIKE OZZY OSBOURNE.

GOD CREATED THE UNIVERSE BY LIGHTING A FART. BUT THEN, WHO DOESN'T HAVE THE CONTENTS OF THEIR WORLD FALL FROM THEIR ASS AT LEAST ONCE EVERY SATURDAY MORNING? GOD MADE WOMAN BY PUTTING A VAGINA ON A MAN AND USED A COUPLE OF BOOBS FROM THE SPARE BOOB DRAWER. HIS RECEPTIONIST IS CALLED KAREN.

AND SATAN? WHEN PETER SAID HE WOULD SELL HIS SOUL TO BE FAMOUS, SATAN WAS ALL SET TO MAKE THE CLAIM, BEFORE HIS SECRETARY TOLD HIM THAT PETER HAD ALREADY SOLD HIS SOUL FOR BEE GEES TICKETS, AND AGAIN FOR HALF OF A MALLOMAR CHOCOLATE COOKIE.

HARVESTER OF THE SOULS OF THE DEAD, DEATH LIVES WITH HIS MOTHER, HAS ASTHMA AND IS ABOUT AS GOOD AT SMALL TALK WITH WOMEN AS HENRY THE VIII'S EXECUTIONER. IT'S DIFFICULT TO PLACE HIS LACK OF SUCCESS, BUT IT MIGHT HAVE SOMETHING TO DO WITH HIS 'LOOK': BLACK ROBE, HIS HEAD ADORNED WITH SPIDERS AND SNAKES WHICH SLITHER IN AND OUT OF HIS EYE SOCKETS, MOUTH AND EAR HOLES. IT'S JUST SO EIGHTIES.

DEATH DOESN'T LIKE BEING DEAD AND HATES THE FACT THAT HE DOESN'T HAVE ANY BUTTOCKS, LIKE POSH SPICE. HOWEVER, HE REMAINS ONE OF THE MOST POWERFUL FORCES IN THE UNIVERSE: THE LIVING DIE WHEN HE MAKES PHYSICAL CONTACT WITH THEM. HE IS, HOWEVER, NOWHERE NEAR AS POWERFUL AS ELTON JOHN WHO NEEDS ONLY SOUND TO CREATE THE LIVING DEAD.

DEATH DRIVES A YELLOW VOLKSWAGEN BEETLE AND HAS A DOG CHARGED WITH HARVESTING THE SOULS OF DEAD DOGS. NOW SURELY THEY COULD HAVE MADE IT TO THE SET OF TURNER & HOOCH TOGETHER? A) THAT'S JUST RESPONSIBLY ECO AND B) HE WOULD HAVE SAVED US FROM 'SLEEPLESS IN SEATTLE' AND 'YOU'VE GOT MAIL'. COME ON DEATH, LET'S HUSTLE!

Death
IS A
BITCH!

CHRIS GRIFFIN

PROFILE & INTERVIEW

CHRIS GRIFFIN

CHRIS REALLY LOOKS UP TO HIS DAD, PETER. HE IDOLISES THE MAN. IN FACT, IN 'BOYS DO CRY' WHEN PETER SHOWS HIM HIS BELT BUCKLE WHICH SAYS: 'EVERYTHING'S BIGGER IN TEXAS', CHRIS ENTHUSES: "BELTS ARE A GREAT WAY TO EXPRESS YOUR OPINIONS." SEEMED FUNNIER IN THE SHOW, BUT I GUESS THAT'S WHAT HAPPENS WHEN YOU'VE GOT MOVING IMAGES INSTEAD OF BEING TRAPPED BY THE CONFINES OF STILLS AND THE WRITTEN WORD, LIKE ANDY CAPP. OH, THAT LOVEABLE, WIFE-BEATING ALCOHOLIC.

HE ONCE BELIEVED HIS LOW GRADES IN MATHEMATICS WERE SELF-INFLICTED AFTER TICKLING HIS BRAIN BY STICKING AN ARMY MAN'S RIFLE UP HIS NOSE AND ACCIDENTALLY PUNCTURING A LOBE.

IF CHRIS HAD TO CHOOSE BETWEEN HIS MAM AND DAD, LIKE IN 'KRAMER V KRAMER', HE'D GO FOR PETER. WHEN, IN 'LETHAL WEAPONS', PETER AND LOIS WERE HAVING A FIST FIGHT, CHRIS CHEERED 'KICK HER ASS!' IN 'STEWIE GRIFFIN: THE UNTOLD STORY', WHEN LOIS AND PETER ARE HAVING SOME 'ADULT TIME', THE CHILDREN MISTOOK IT FOR A FIGHT AND CHRIS TOLD MEG: 'I DON'T KNOW WHAT THEY'RE FIGHTING ABOUT, BUT I THINK DAD'S WINNING. GO DAD!'

IN SEASON SIX'S 'PETARDED' (BASED ON SEAN PENN'S ULTIMATELY FUTILE ATTEMPT AT WINNING AN OSCAR IN 'I AM SAM', HE DID HOWEVER, WALK THE AWARD FOR 'EASILY THE MOST CLOYING MOVIE IN THE HISTORY OF MOVIES'), AFTER PETER WINS A GAME OF TRIVIAL PURSUIT, CHRIS TELLS MEG: 'MY DAD IS SMARTER THAN YOUR DAD', TO WHICH MEG REPLIES, 'WE HAVE THE SAME DAD, IDIOT!' CHRIS RESPONDS WITH 'YEAH, BUT MINE'S SMARTER'. CHRIS, HE'S A LOVELY LITTLE BALL OF BOY.

CHRIS IS NOT FANTASTIC AROUND GIRLS. THINKING HE'LL BE REJECTED BECAUSE THEY WON'T LIKE WHAT THEY SEE. OR, THEY'LL SEE HIS SCROTUM AND SEE THAT IT HAS A SEAM ON IT AND THEN THEY'LL THINK HE'S MADE UP OF TWO DIFFERENT GUYS THAT WERE SEWN TOGETHER... WELL THAT'S WHAT HE THINKS HAPPENED TO HIM!

FUN FACTS

FACTFILE

AGE: 1 (EIGHT SEASONS)

PLACE OF BIRTH: QUAHOG, RHODE ISLAND

BIRTH NAME: CHRISTOPHER CROSS GRIFFIN

GENDER: LARDBOY

MEET... CHRIS GRIFFIN

CHRIS GRIFFIN WALKS INTO THE ROOM AND HE'S A LITTLE PRE-OCCUPIED. PERHAPS HE'S A LITTLE UNCOMFORTABLE WHERE HE'S SAT, THE SUN MAY BE IN HIS EYES OR HE'S JUST A LITTLE NERVOUS AND WOULD LIKE A DRINK OF WATER.

OR THE REASON MAY BE A LITTLE MORE STRAIGHTFORWARD. HE HAS PROBABLY PEED IN HIS PANTS!.

IT MUST BE DIFFICULT FOR CHRIS GRIFFIN. A YOUNG MAN WITH THE WORLD AT HIS FEET BUT AS AN ACTOR IT COULD BE A REAL CHALLENGE TO LIVE UP TO THE FAMILY GUY STEREOTYPE OF BEING MENTALLY RETARDED AND A LITTLE ONE-DIMENSIONAL. BUT HE IS UP TO THE TASK!

CHRIS LOVES HIS FAMILY BUT ESPECIALLY HIS MOM WHO HE REGARDS AS HOT! HE ALSO STANDS UP FOR THEM - AND ONCE TOLD HIS DAD NOT TO FIGHT HUGH GRANT "BECAUSE HE IS BIGGER THAN YOU". DESPITE HAVING A MIND OF HIS OWN HE DOES ADMIT THAT HE LIKES BEING TOLD WHAT TO DO.

CHRIS IS A FILM BUFF WHO WOULD LOVE TO BE AN ARTIST. HE WOULD ALSO LIKE TO FALL IN LOVE - HE HAS HAD A FLING WITH CONNIE D'AMICO AT HIGH SCHOOL, ALYSSA THE REPUBLICAN, ANNA THE VET INTERN AND LOKA CHIEF'S DAUGHTER.

CHRIS DOES HAVE A MORTAL FEAR OF HIS CLOSET AND THE EVIL MONKEY WHO LURKS IN THERE. BUT HE KNOWS MONKEY WASN'T ALWAYS EVIL. HE'S ALSO HAPPY WITH HIS INVISIBLE FRIEND, COL. SCHWARTZ.

THE LIFE AND TIMES OF CHRIS GRIFFIN...

CHRIS: I DON'T WANT TO GET RID OF MY PIMPLE, I LIKE HIM. HE'S MY FRIEND. HIS NAME IS DOUG.

BRIAN: I JUST WISH I DIDN'T HAVE TO LOOK AT IT.

CHRIS: WELL, WE HAVE TO LOOK AT YOUR ANUS ALL DAY!

STEWIE: IF YOUR TEACHERS ASK ABOUT YOUR BRUISES, WHAT DO YOU TELL THEM?

CHRIS: I GOT HIT BY A BASEBALL.

LOIS: CHRIS, WE KNOW WHAT YOU DID.

CHRIS: YOU MEAN THAT I LIED ABOUT MY AGE TO GET INTO AN INDIAN CASINO?

LOIS: NO.

CHRIS: YOU MEAN ABOUT THE TIME I HAD HARD GAS AND POOED MYSELF?

PETER: CLOSE, BUT NO.

STEWIE: HOW IS THAT CLOSE?

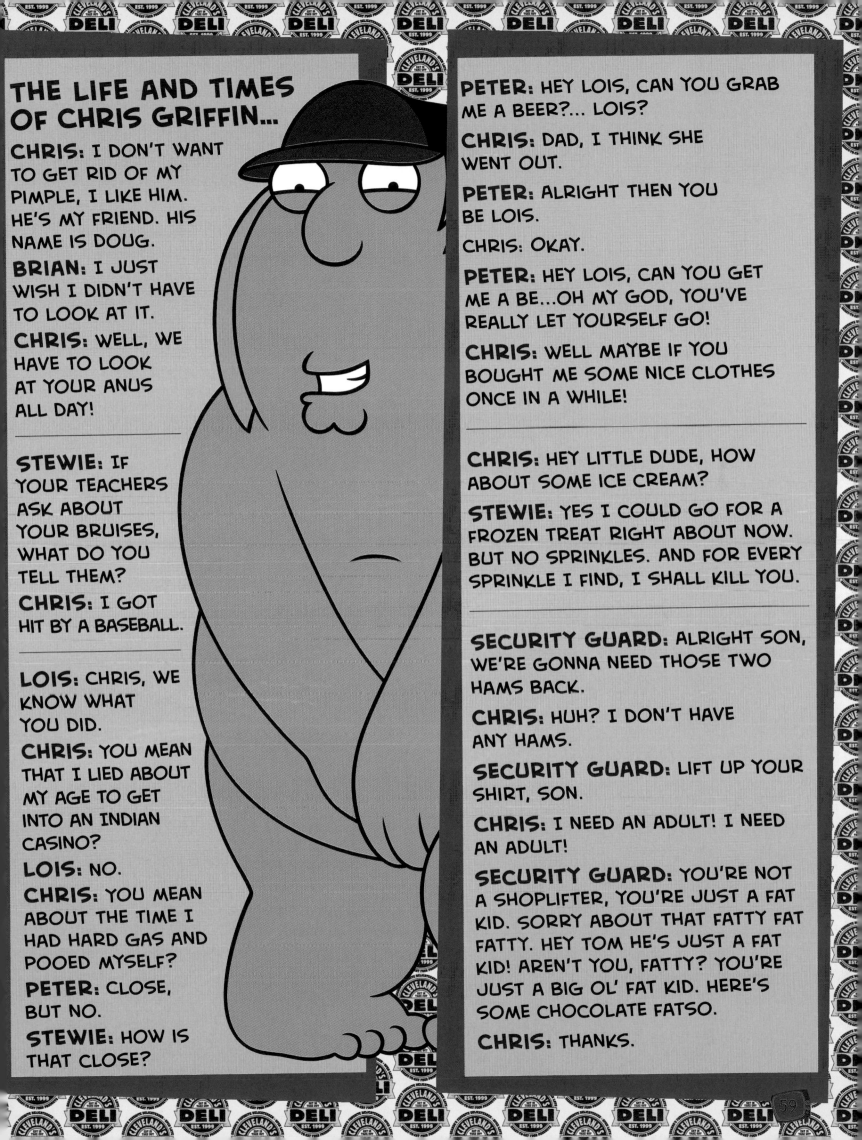

PETER: HEY LOIS, CAN YOU GRAB ME A BEER?... LOIS?

CHRIS: DAD, I THINK SHE WENT OUT.

PETER: ALRIGHT THEN YOU BE LOIS.

CHRIS: OKAY.

PETER: HEY LOIS, CAN YOU GET ME A BE...OH MY GOD, YOU'VE REALLY LET YOURSELF GO!

CHRIS: WELL MAYBE IF YOU BOUGHT ME SOME NICE CLOTHES ONCE IN A WHILE!

CHRIS: HEY LITTLE DUDE, HOW ABOUT SOME ICE CREAM?

STEWIE: YES I COULD GO FOR A FROZEN TREAT RIGHT ABOUT NOW. BUT NO SPRINKLES. AND FOR EVERY SPRINKLE I FIND, I SHALL KILL YOU.

SECURITY GUARD: ALRIGHT SON, WE'RE GONNA NEED THOSE TWO HAMS BACK.

CHRIS: HUH? I DON'T HAVE ANY HAMS.

SECURITY GUARD: LIFT UP YOUR SHIRT, SON.

CHRIS: I NEED AN ADULT! I NEED AN ADULT!

SECURITY GUARD: YOU'RE NOT A SHOPLIFTER, YOU'RE JUST A FAT KID. SORRY ABOUT THAT FATTY FAT FATTY. HEY TOM HE'S JUST A FAT KID! AREN'T YOU, FATTY? YOU'RE JUST A BIG OL' FAT KID. HERE'S SOME CHOCOLATE FATSO.

CHRIS: THANKS.

PETER: (SLAPPING THE BACK OF CHRIS'S HEAD) CHRIS IS NOT AS SMART AS YOU THINK HE IS...

CHRIS: HEY!

PETER: HE DID IT. (POINTS TO A FLOOR LAMP, AND CHRIS STARTS FIGHTING WITH IT.)

CHRIS: DOCTOR, I NEED YOU TO GET RID OF THIS ZIT!

DOUG: (CHRIS'S ZIT) YOU TRAITOR!

DOCTOR: WHOA, THAT'S A DOOSIE! I BET SOME OF THOSE AWFUL KIDS AT SCHOOL CALL YOU ZIT FACE?

CHRIS: NO

DOCTOR: PAPA ZIT?

CHRIS: NO

DOCTOR: PUS PEAK?

CHRIS: NO

DOCTOR: FAT ASS?

CHRIS: WELL.. YEAH..

DOCTOR: TSK, TSK..OH, THAT'S TERRIBLE!

CHRIS: DAD, CAN YOU HELP ME WITH MY MATHS HOMEWORK?

PETER: MATHS? MATHS MY DEAR BOY IS NOTHING MORE THAN THE LESBIAN SISTER OF BIOLOGY.

CHRIS: SO... WHAT ARE YOU WEARING? HA HA HA HA HA WOW! I BET YOU COULD SEE RIGHT THROUGH THAT.

LOIS: CHRIS, WHO ARE YOU TALKING TO?

CHRIS: GRANDMA.

CHRIS: MY NAME IS CHRIS, I'M SUPPOSED TO BE ON MY BEST BEHAVIOUR TONIGHT AND NOT MENTION POO... OH GOD, WHAT HAVE I DONE?

CHRIS: YOU'RE JUST RUNNING AWAY FROM YOUR TROUBLES BY BEING HERE!

PETER: WHAT ARE YOU TALKING ABOUT? MEG'S RIGHT HERE.

CHRIS: DAD, I TRIED TO GO TO SCHOOL BUT THIS GUY WON'T LET ME.

PETER: OH YEAH? HIM AND WHAT ARMY?

CHRIS: THE U.S. ARMY.

PETER: OH, THAT'S A GOOD ARMY.

CHRIS: DAD, YOU SHOULD INVENT THE FRISBEE, THAT'S AN AWESOME TOY.

MEG: CHRIS, THE FRISBEE IS ALREADY INVENTED.

CHRIS: THEN HOW COME I NEVER HEARD OF IT?

CHRIS: MY DAD IS SMARTER THAN YOUR DAD.

MEG: WE HAVE THE SAME DAD IDIOT!

CHRIS: YEAH, BUT MINE'S SMARTER!

CHRIS: (ANSWERING THE PHONE THE PHONE):

STEPHENSON RESIDENCE.

LOIS: CHRIS, WE'VE GONE THROUGH THIS BEFORE. IT'S PRONOUNCED GRIFFIN.

MEG: CHRIS HAVE YOU LOST WEIGHT? YOU LOOK WICKED SKINNY! I'M JEALOUS!

CHRIS: REALLY? CAUSE... CAUSE I'M JEALOUS OF YOUR MOUSTACHE!

MEG: I DON'T HAVE A MOUSTACHE!

FAMILY GUY FACTS

HEY, YOU WANNA KNOW HAWAII FIVE-O FACTS ABOUT THE SWEETEST FREAKIN' SHOW ON TV? THEN GO OUT AND GET THE LITTLE HOUSE ON THE PRAIRIE ANNUAL AND STOP WASTING OUR TIME. HERE'S 50 THINGS WE DON'T CARE WHETHER YOU KNEW ABOUT FAMILY GUY...

1. FAMILY GUY FIRST AIRED JANUARY 31, 1999.

2. FAMILY GUY WAS CANCELLED IN 2000 AND AGAIN IN 2002 BUT DVD SALES, MIXED WITH THE POPULARITY OF CARTOON NETWORK RE-RUNS, CONVINCED FOX TO RESUME THE SHOW IN 2005.

3. PLANS REMAIN AFOOT TO BRING FAMILY GUY TO THE BIG SCREEN WITH SETH MACFARLANE TALKING ABOUT A SOUND OF MUSIC-TYPE MUSICAL!

4. FAMILY GUY AND ITS CAST HAVE BEEN NOMINATED FOR EIGHT EMMY AWARDS AND WON THREE - SETH MACFARLANE FOR VOICEOVER WORK, WALTER MURPHY FOR MUSIC AND LYRICS, AND STEVEN FONTI FOR ANIMATION.

5. ENTERTAINMENT WEEKLY TOOK UMBRAGE TO FAMILY GUY USING A COPY OF THEIR RAG AS TOILET PAPER AND THE TIME STEWIE GRIFFIN SNAPPED THE NECK OF A REPORTER FOR THE MAGAZINE.

6. THE SHOW IS CRITICIZED FOR USING STORY IDEAS AND HUMOUR SIMILAR TO THOSE IN EPISODES THE SIMPSONS. MACFARLANE RESPONDED TO THE CRITICISM ON DVD, SAYING IT WAS COMPLETELY FOUNDED AND TRUE.

7. QUAHOG IS ALSO THE NAME OF AN EDIBLE CLAM.

8. LOIS WAS ORIGINALLY DRAWN AS A BLONDE, BEFORE BECOMING A REDHEAD.

9. FG WAS NO. 5 IN CHANNEL 4'S 100 GREATEST CARTOONS POLL, BEHIND THE SIMPSONS, TOM AND JERRY, SOUTH PARK AND THE TOY STORY FILMS.

10. JOE WAS AN OCTOPUS IN A PREVIOUS LIFE. QUAGMIRE WAS JACK THE RIPPER IN A PREVIOUS LIFE. GIGGITY.

11. STEWIE'S HALF-BROTHER BERTRAM WAS BORN TO TWO LESBIANS AFTER PETER DONATED SPERM.

12. THE CHARACTERS OF PETER AND BRIAN ARE VERY SIMILAR TO PREDECESSORS LARRY AND STEVE, WRITTEN AND DIRECTED BY SETH MACFARLANE. THE SHOW FEATURED A MORONIC MAN WHO ADOPTS A TALKING DOG AND PUTS THE DOG THROUGH HELL.

13. THE THREE SKYSCRAPERS SEEN BEHIND THE GRIFFIN'S HOUSE ARE ONE FINANCIAL CENTER, 50 KENNEDY PLAZA AND THE BANK OF AMERICA TOWER IN PROVIDENCE, RHODE ISLAND.

14. CLEVELAND'S ULTIMATE WOMAN IS MARGARET THATCHER.

15. BRIAN'S VOICE IS SIMPLY SETH MACFARLANE SPEAKING NORMALLY.

16. MACFARLANE BASED THE VOICE OF PETER GRIFFIN ON A SECURITY GUARD HE KNEW WHILE AT COLLEGE.

17. THE ORIGINAL TITLES OF EPISODES IN THE FIRST SERIES WERE BASED ON 1940S MYSTERY RADIO SHOWS WHICH IS WHY THEY HAD REFERENCES TO DEATH IN THEM.

18. WHEN THE SHOW WAS CANCELLED A SECOND TIME, IN 2003, THERE WAS AN ONLINE PETITION WITH OVER 100,000 NAMES ON IT TO SAVE THE SHOW.

19. SETH GREEN SAYS THAT THE VOICE OF CHRIS IS BASED ON TED LEVINE'S PERFORMANCE AS BUFFALO BILL IN 'SILENCE OF THE LAMBS'.

20. THE CHARACTER OF NEIL GOLDMAN, THE BOY WHO PERENNIALLY CHASES MEG, IS NAMED AFTER ONE OF THE SHOW'S WRITERS.

21. SETH MACFARLANE'S FAVOURITE FAMILY GUY MOMENT IS THE SCENE FROM 'DA BOOM' WHERE PETER IS FEEDING TOM SELLECK. (NONE FOR YOU HIGGINS).

22. THIS SERIES IS BANNED IN INDONESIA, TAIWAN, VIETNAM, IRAN, SOUTH KOREA, SOUTH AFRICA, AND MALAYSIA.

23. PETER'S DRINK OF CHOICE IS PAWTUCKET PATRIOT ALE.

24. ALL OF THE HIGH-END HOTELS SEEN ON THE SHOW HAVE BARRINGTON IN THEIR NAME. SERIES CREATOR SETH MACFARLANE HAS STATED THEY ARE NAMED AFTER THE CITY OF BARRINGTON, RHODE ISLAND, A VERY UPSCALE COMMUNITY.

25. THE BIG CHICKEN THAT ALWAYS FIGHTS PETER IS NAMED ERNIE.

26. EVERY EPISODE INCLUDES AT LEAST ONE INSTANCE OF ONE CHARACTER SAYING 'WHAT THE HELL...' TO ANOTHER.

27. SETH MACFARLANE HAS ADMITTED THAT THE FAMILY'S CONSTANT ABUSE OF MEG IS A RESULT OF 'A BUNCH OF MALE WRITERS NOT KNOWING HOW TO WRITE FOR A TEENAGE GIRL'.

28. SETH MACFARLANE WAS GIVEN VOICE TRAINING BY A 90 YEAR OLD COUPLE WHO ALSO TRAINED FRANK SINATRA

29. CHRIS LOST HIS EARRING IN SERIES THREE.

30. ON THE MORNING OF SEPTEMBER 11, 2001, SETH MACFARLANE WAS BOOKED ON AMERICAN AIRLINES FLIGHT 11 TO FLY FROM BOSTON TO LA. HIS TRAVEL AGENT, HOWEVER, MIXED UP THE DEPARTURE TIME AND HE ARRIVED AT LOGAN AIRPORT 30 MINUTES LATE. FLIGHT 11 CRASHED INTO THE NORTH TOWER OF THE WORLD TRADE CENTER.

31. DEATH IS VOICED BY ADAM CARROLLA, DEATH DOG IS VOICED BY JIMMEL KIMMEL AND THE BLACK KNIGHT IS VOICED BY WILL FERRELL.

32. SETH MACFARLANE DOES THE VOICES FOR PETER GRIFFIN, STEWIE GRIFFIN, BRIAN GRIFFIN AND GLENN QUAGMIRE.

33. UP UNTIL THE END OF SEASON SEVEN THERE HAD BEEN 126 EPISODES OF FAMILY GUY.

34. PETER WAS BORN IN MEXICO, HIS REAL FATHER WAS IRISH AND IS CERTIFIED RETARDED.

35. QUAGMIRE, BORN 1947, SAYS HIS SECRET TO LONGEVITY IS CARROTS INSERTED INTO HIS BODY THROUGH EVERY ORIFICE.

36. THE PARENTS TELEVISION COUNCIL WANTS FOX TO REMOVE IT FROM THEIR SCHEDULE – MACFARLANE DESCRIBED IT THUS: "THAT'S LIKE GETTING HATE MAIL FROM HITLER. THEY'RE LITERALLY TERRIBLE HUMAN BEINGS."

37. IN SERIES SEVEN, BRIAN'S NOVEL 'FASTER THAN THE SPEED OF LOVE', IS PUBLISHED AND BREAKS A RECORD BY NOT SELLING A SINGLE COPY.

38. BRIAN IS PRONE TO ALCOHOLISM. AS WELLS AS MARTINIS, HE DRINKS PAWTUCKET PATRIOT ALE, JACK DANIELS, JAGERMEISTER AND MOJITOS.

39. SERIES SEVEN'S EPISODE 'THREE KINGS' PARODIES MOVIES 'STAND BY ME', 'MISERY' AND 'THE SHAWSHANK REDEMPTION'.

40. A FAMILY GUY VIDEO GAME WAS RELEASED IN 2006. THE GAME IS SPLIT INTO 22 LEVELS FOR THE THREE PLAYABLE CHARACTERS: BRIAN, PETER OR STEWIE.

41. SETH MACFARLANE DECIDED THAT BRIAN WOULD BE ABLE TO UNDERSTAND STEWIE. OTHER ADULTS UNDERSTAND STEWIE BUT IGNORE WHATEVER HE SAYS BECAUSE HE IS A BABY.

42. IN THE 10,00TH ISSUE OF MAGAZINE ENTERTAINMENT WEEKLY, BRIAN WAS SELECTED AS THE DOG FOR 'THE PERFECT TV FAMILY'.

43. QUAGMIRE'S VOICE IS BASED ON A FAST-TALKING 1950S AMERICAN RADIO JOCKEY.

44. JILLIAN RUSSELL, BRIAN'S MENTALLY CHALLENGED FORMER GIRLFRIEND, IS VOICE BY E.T. AND CHARLIE'S ANGELS' DREW BARRYMORE.

45. FAMILY GUY EVEN HAS ITS OWN BITCHIN' PINBALL MACHINE. RELEASED IN 2007, IT HAS A TV CHALLENGE DROP HOLE, BEER CAN GIANT TARGET, EVIL MONKEY'S LAIR RAMP AND STEWIE'S MINI PINBALL.

46. QUAHOG IS MODELLED ON CRANSTON, RHODE ISLAND.

47. THERE'S EVEN A QUAHOG BASED FAMILY GUY MONOPOLY!

48. IF YOU'RE LOOKING FOR INTERVIEWS WITH THE CAST OF FAMILY GUY, CHECK OUT ITUNES. THERE ARE 28 AUDIO-ONLY PODCASTS THERE.

49. FAMILY GUY SEASON EIGHT KICKED OFF WITH 'SOMETHING, SOMETHING, SOMETHING DARK SIDE'. AN EMPIRE STRIKES BACK SEQUEL TO THE INSANELY POPULAR STAR WARS-THEMED 'BLUE HARVEST'.

50. DON'T WORRY. FAMILY GUY IS CONTRACTED TO MAKE NEW EPISODES UNTIL AT LEAST 2012.

FAMILY GUY

BRIAN
PROFILE &
GRIFFIN
INTERVIEW

STOP YANKIN' MY CHAIN!

67

BRIAN GRIFFIN

BRIAN'S FATHER WAS RUN OVER BY A MILK TRUCK AND HIS MOTHER PUT HIM UP FOR ADOPTION, OR RATHER GAVE HIM AWAY IN A CARDBOARD BOX LINED WITH A DIRTY TOWEL.

RHODES ISLAND'S BROWN UNIVERSITY COUNT BRIAN AMONGST ITS ALUMNI.

IN RESPONSE TO STEWIE'S RUMOURED GAYNESS, BRIAN SIMPLY RESPONDS: "NOT YET, BUT BE PATIENT."

ATHEISM IS BRIAN'S PREFERRED WORLD VIEW. WHEN MEG ATTEMPTED TO CONVERT HIM TO THE BIBLE, HE ASKED HER WHY GOD WOULD PUT HER ON THE EARTH WITH AN UNATTRACTIVE BODY, NEGLECTFUL FAMILY, AND ABUSIVE FATHER. SHE GAVE UP RELIGION.

NEITHER GENITALS NOR ANUS ARE OUT OF BOUNDS FOR BRIAN'S TONGUE.

FACTFILE

AGE: 8
(THAT'S 42 IN DOG YEARS).

PLACE OF BIRTH:
AUSTIN, TEXAS

BIRTH NAME: BRIAN GRIFFIN

GENDER: STRAY

BRIAN DOESN'T USUALLY
'DO' REGULAR DOGS.
BUT HE WAS ONCE
ACCUSED OF
IMPREGNATING
CARTER
PEWTERSCHMIDT'S
RACING DOG, SEABREEZE.
HOWEVER, IT TURNED
OUT THAT HE HAD BEEN
FALSELY ACCUSED
OF DOING THE DIRTY DEED.

BRIAN FOUND HIS MOTHER, BISCUIT,
IN TEXAS, STUFFED
AND BEING USED AS A TABLE.

DESPITE BEING MAN'S BEST
FRIEND AND CONSTANTLY
LOOKING OUT FOR PETER'S
BEST INTERESTS, WHEN HIS
MASTER BUILT AN INDOOR
WATER SLIDE BY RUNNING
WATER DOWN THE HOUSE STAIRS
AND PROMPTLY INJURED HIMSELF,
BRIAN WAS NOT IMPRESSED. HE
TOLD PETER: "I'M NOT GOING
TO TAKE YOU TO THE HOSPITAL
BECAUSE IF I DO, YOU WON'T
LEARN ANYTHING."

FUN
FACTS

MEET... BRIAN GRIFFIN

BRIAN GRIFFIN HAS AS MANY PERSONALITIES AS HE HAS LEGS. HE IS OFTEN ABLE TO STAND ON JUST TWO OF THOSE LEGS, SHOWING HOW HE IS A DIGNIFIED INDIVIDUAL COMMITTED TO THE FINER THINGS IN LIFE: GOOD WOMEN, GOOD WINE AND GOOD SQUEEZY PLASTIC BONES.

MIND YOU, HE WAS A STRAY BEFORE JOINING THE GRIFFIN FAMILY AND HE IS STILL NOT AVERSE TO EATING THE ODD PIECE OF GARBAGE OR BEING A BIT WORRIED ABOUT THE VACUUM CLEANER.

DESPITE BEING MAN'S BEST FRIEND – ALBEIT A TALKING ONE – HE PLOTS THE MURDER OF HIS MASTER WHILST EYING UP THE WOMAN OF THE HOUSE.

IS HE RACIAL? WELL, HE HAS BEEN KNOWN TO BARK AT A BLACK RAP ARTIST. IS HE A BIT STRANGE? WELL, HE ADMITS TO SLIPPING ON LOIS' DRESSES AND SLIDING INTO HER STILETTOS.

HE HAS A LOVE–HATE RELATIONSHIP WITH STEWIE. MOST OF THE TIME HE LOVES TO HATE HIM.

THE LIFE AND TIMES OF BRIAN GRIFFIN

PETER: AWW MAN! I HATE TRIVIAL PURSUIT, IT ALWAYS MAKES ME FEEL SO STUPID.

BRIAN: MORE STUPID THEN THAT TIME YOU LOCKED YOUR KEYS OUT OF THE CAR?

BRIAN: YOU'RE REALLY GOING TO TAKE BACK DONATED PRESENTS ON CHRISTMAS EVE?

PETER: YEP, NOW HERE'S THE PLAN: YOU'LL ENTER THROUGH THE AIR CONDITIONING DUCT HERE. NOW THERE'LL BE AN INVISIBLE LASER

GRID THREE INCHES FROM THE FLOOR, SO YOU'LL HAVE TO COMPRESS YOUR BODY TO THE SIZE OF AN ORDINARY HOUSEHOLD SPONGE AND SLIDE UNDERNEATH LIKE SOME KIND OF WEIRD AMPHIBIOUS DOLPHIN.

BRIAN: CAN I BUY SOME POT FROM YOU?

PETER: SO DID YOUR THERAPIST FIGURE OUT WHAT THE PROBLEM WAS?

BRIAN: YEAH. HE THINKS I'M IN LOVE.

PETER: OH MY GOD... YOU CAN TALK!

LOIS: TOGETHER WE CAN DO ANYTHING: FACE ANY FOE, OVERCOME ANY OBSTACLE.

PETER: YEAH, CLIMB ANY MOUNTAIN, RENT ANY VIDEO, DIAL ANY PHONE. AND NOT JUST OUR PHONE, LOIS, OTHER PEOPLE'S PHONES. DECENT PHONES, GOD-FEARING PHONES, PHONES THAT EVERYBODY ELSE GAVE UP ON, BUT WE KNEW BETTER BECAUSE WE WERE A TEAM!

BRIAN: WHAT THE HELL ARE YOU TALKING ABOUT?

BRIAN: HOLA, ME LLAMO ES BRIAN ... NOSOTROS QUEREMOS IR CON USTEDES...

BELLBOY: (SPANISH) HEY, THAT WAS PRETTY GOOD, EXCEPT WHEN YOU SAID "ME LLAMO ES BRIAN," YOU DON'T NEED THE "ES," JUST ME LLAMO BRIAN.

BRIAN: OH, YOU SPEAK ENGLISH!

BELLBOY: (SIGH) NO, JUST THAT FIRST SPEECH AND THIS ONE EXPLAINING IT.

BRIAN: YOU'RE KIDDING ME, RIGHT?

BELLBOY: (SPANISH) QUE?

CHRIS: I DON'T CARE WHAT SHE SAYS, I'M NEVER GOING BACK!

BRIAN: LOOK YOU CAN'T RUN AWAY FROM YOUR PROBLEMS CHRIS. THAT'S WHAT I TRIED TO DO. I JOINED THE PEACE CORPS AND A DAY LATER I WAS TWO CONTINENTS AWAY.

CHRIS: REALLY?

HIIIIII! ADOLF HERE! ADOLF WHO? OH, YOUUUU! IT'S BEEN A LONG TIME ZINCE ICH HAF BEEN ON DER FRUNT PAGES OF GUTENTAG MAGAZUNT YOU KNOW, TOO LONG! DANKE TO DOSE FAMILY GUYS ICH AM BACK! THAT'S B. A. C. H. BACK!

ZER HAF BEEN A LOT OF FAMOUS FACES ON FAMILY GUY, ICH MEAN REALLY FAMOUS, LIKE EINSTEIN, NORRIS, SHATNER, BUT WHEN THEY CONTACTED DER UNDERGROUND MOVEMENT OF EMBARRASSED NAZIS, ASKING ME TO APPEAR IN THE FERRY EINER EPISODE OF FAMILY GUY, ICH TURNED TO DER REST OF THE UMEN AND ASKED THEM HOW MUCH LONGER WE SHOULD BE IN HIDING? WE GOT INTO OUR UBOAT AND BEFORE YOU COULD SAY 'LET'S EXTERMINATE ALL THE JEWS', I WAS BACK DISPLAYING THE FAMOUS GERMAN SENSE OF HUMOUR! AND ALLE IST GUT!

WHEN ICH SAW DER FIRST SCRIPT, ICH TURNED TO GOEBBELS (WHO IST NOW CHARGING EINE FORTUNE FOR DER PR) AND ASKER HIM, WHAT HE THOUGHT. HIS ANSA? WHAT'S THE BROCKWORST THAT CAN HAPPEN OT YOUR IMAGEN? HE HAS EINE POINT. THAT FIRST SKIT, ABOUT ME BEING ANNOYED BY A PHYSICALLY SUPERIOR JEW, DIDN'T GO DOWN WELL WITH HIMMLER. HE HAS NEIN SENSE OF HUMOUR (HE WAS LIVID WHEN HE FOUND OUT WE CALLED THE 'SS' THE SISSY SPACEKS BECAUSE THEY WERE ALWAYS COVERED IN DER BLOOD).

LATER, I THOUGHT MY PERFORMANCE IN 'DEATH IS A BITCH' VER ICH PLAYED A TALK SHOW HOST WITH CHRISTIAN SLATER AS A GUEST, WAS ZER GUT. THAT SLATER IST SUCH A NICE GUY. ICH DON'T THINK ANYONE BEGRUDGES DER FACT THAT HE'S BEEN DOING A JACK NICHOLSON IMPRESSION FOR THIRTY YEARS. I MEAN, DICK CHENEY'S BEEN DOING ME FOR ABOUT THE SAME AMOUNT OF TIME. DER YOU GO. DIE GERMAN HUMOUR IS SER TOPICAL, JAH?

ON DER THEME, HERE COMES ANOTHER OF FAMILY GUY'S STAR TURNS, A VERY, VERY CLOSE RELATIVE... ER, GUT FREUND OF MINE, GEORGE W. BUSH. GEORGE. I HAF ALWAYS WONDERED, WHAT DOES THE W. STANDS FOR IN YOUR NAME? "WHAT?" REALLY? "WHAT?" I SEE. NOW HOW DID A COUNTRY BUBE LIKE YOU COME TO BE PART OF DER FAMILY GUY? IT'S A LITTLE OFF YOUR RADAR, IST IT NEIN?

"OFF MY RADAR? THERE'S ISN'T A FREAKIN'S PLACE ON GOD'S OIL-FILLED EARTH THAT'S OFF MY RADAR, 'PART FROM WEAPONS OF MASS DESTRUCTION, BIN LADEN'S HIDEOUT AND THE SAFE WHERE THEY HIDE THE RECIPE FOR CHEERIOS, TH'IMPORTANT PLACES. I DID FAMILY GUY BECAUSE I STAND FOR FAMILY VALUES: HATE, DISTRUST AND DISAPPOINTMENT. THEY HAD ME LOOK STUPID ON THAT SHOW, BUT THAT'S OKAY, IT'S GOOD TO KEEP THE GENERAL PUBLIC IN THE DARK, AND UNDER

MACHO JOSEPH 'JOE' SWANSON IS A MAN AS SUBJECT TO IRRATIONAL BOUTS OF ANGER AS SAMUEL L. JACKSON (COME ON, HE'S NOT ACTING!).

HIS WIFE BONNIE 'BONNIE' SWANSON IS A WOMAN WHO JUST CAN'T SAY NO TO ANYTHING. AND WE MEAN ANYTHING!

THEIR DAUGHTER SUSIE 'SUSIE' SWANSON, THE OBJECT OF STEWIE AFFECTIONS (AND THE ONE WHO BITCHSLAPPED THE WEE MAN), IS IMPOSSIBLY CUTE, THEIR SON KEVIN 'KEVIN' SWANSON WAS KILLED WHILE ON DUTY IN IRAQ. HE WOULD HAVE EVENTUALLY BEEN SLAUGHTERED BY JOE. LIKE ANY GOOD, TRUE PHYSICALLY ABUSIVE REPUBLICAN FATHER, BEFORE HIS DEATH, JOE PUSHED KEVIN RIGHT TO THE LIMIT. IN FACT, JOE ONCE CONFESSED THAT THE FIRST TIME KEVIN BEAT HIM AT A COMPETITION HE GAVE HIM: "A SMALL CONGRATULATORY PUNCH, FOLLOWED BY A FEW MORE, THEN EVERYTHING GOT A LITTLE HAZY AND KEVIN HAD TO GO AND LIVE WITH A FOSTER FAMILY FOR A WHILE." NO ONE REALLY KNOWS HOW KEVIN DIED. BUT THEN NO ONE KNOWS WHY MADONNA KEEPS ON PERFORMING EVEN THOUGH SHE LOOKS LIKE AN ALBINO PRUNE THAT'S HAD ALL THE JUICY LIFE SUCKED OUT OF IT.

OKAY, SO JOE MIGHT BE OVER-ZEALOUS, HAVE A TEMPER SHORTER THAN A JEHOVAH WITNESS' CHRISTMAS CARD LIST AND A BY-THE-NUMBERS ATTITUDE BUT HE'S A MAN WHO SETS THE BAR HIGHER FOR HIMSELF THAN ANYONE ELSE. WHICH IS KINDA UNFORTUNATE (FILL IN YOUR OWN WHEELCHAIR GAG HERE YOU SICKO).

DESPITE HIS DISABILITIES, JOE IS A SUPERCOP - ONE PART KNIGHTRIDER, ONE PART QUINCY, ONE PART STARSKY, ONE PART HUTCH AND FIFTY PARTS IRONSIDE.

BUT THERE HAVE BEEN TIMES WHEN EVEN THIS STRONG ARM OF THE LAW HAS DOUBTED HIS ABILITIES. LIKE WHEN THE THIEF ESCAPED IN 'READY, WILLING AND DISABLED'. SURE, TO MAKE HIMSELF FEEL BETTER, HE ENTERED AND WON THE DECATHLON IN THE SPECIAL PEOPLE'S GAMES, BECAME A SPORTS CELEBRITY, WON HUGE ENDORSEMENTS AND HAD AN ABC SPECIAL MADE BUT WAS HE HAPPY?

HAPPY? OF COURSE HE WAS HAPPY. HE WAS HAPPIER THAN THAT TIME BUGS BUNNY GOT THE ALL CLEAR FROM THE MYXOMATOSIS CLINIC AFTER MIXING HIS TOASTIES. OKAY, JOE MIGHT HAVE BEEN CAUGHT FOR DOING STEROIDS, BUT IT NEVER DID LEX LUGER'S CAREER ANY HARM, NOW DID IT?

JOE HAS TRIED MANY TIMES TO REGAIN HIS ABILITY TO WALK. HE HAS GOTTEN NEW LEGS AFTER PETER ATE THEM (JOE AND PETER WERE STARVING WHILE FLOATING ON A RAFT MADE OF BLOW-UP SEX DOLLS). UNFORTUNATELY, THE GUY WHO JOE GOT THE LEGS FROM WAS ALSO PARALYZED.

BONNIE SWANSON, IS JOE'S LONG-SUFFERING WIFE WHO, SINCE JOE'S ACCIDENTS HAS NEVER BEEN TRULY SATISFIED AS A WOMAN. GIGGITY. GIGGITY. GOO.

FACTS ABOUT THE SWANSONS

- JOE BECAME PARAPLEGIC AFTER FALLING FROM AN ORPHANAGE ROOF WHILE ATTEMPTING TO APPREHEND THE GRINCH, WHO WAS STEALING CHRISTMAS PRESENTS.

- BONNIE SWANSON WAS PREGNANT FROM HER FIRST APPEARANCE IN 'A HERO SITS NEXT DOOR' IN SEASON ONE UNTIL 'OCEAN'S THREE AND A HALF' IN SEASON SEVEN.

- BONNIE SWANSON IS VOICED BY ACTRESS/POKER PROFESSIONAL JENNIFER TILLY WHO'S WORKED ON 'LIAR, LIAR', 'STUART LITTLE' AND PLAY'S MIKEY'S GIRLFRIEND CELIA IN 'MONSTERS INC'.

- SETH MACFARLANE DECIDED TO KILL KEVIN SWANSON OFF BECAUSE: 'THERE IS ABSOLUTELY NOTHING INTERESTING ABOUT KEVIN. HE'S JUST A BORING CHARACTER.' JOE WAS FURIOUS, BUT COULDN'T CATCH SETH.

THE QUAGMIRES ARE JUST LIKE ANY NORMAL, HAPPY AMERICAN LOVE STORY.

SHE, A MAID WON FOR A WEEK BY PETER AS A WHEEL OF FORTUNE PRIZE, HE A REGISTERED SEX OFFENDER; SHE A WOMAN WHO FELL ALMOST IMMEDIATELY FOR QUAGMIRE'S RAT PACK CHARM, HE A MAN WITH A HAREM OF THAI GIRLS CHAINED UP IN HIS GARAGE WHO, EVERY NIGHT, GENTLY CRY TO BE RELEASED BACK INTO THE WELCOMING BOSOM OF BANGKOK'S RED LIGHT DISTRICT.

THE QUAGMIRES' COURTSHIP WAS SHORTER THAN A FANTASY ISLAND WELCOMING COMMITTEE; THEY MET AND MARRIED BEFORE YOU COULD SAY 'OVER-FAMILIAR WEDDING PHOTOGRAPHER' BUT GLENN KNEW IT WAS ULTIMATELY DOOMED AFTER A BRIEF GLIMPSE OF LOIS GRIFFIN'S TASTY BOOB.

EVEN SO, YOU CAN'T KNOCK THE GUY: HE TRIED TO CLEAN UP HIS ACT TO MAINTAIN WEDLOCK. BUT YOU KNOW, THAT TASTY BOOB JUST WOULDN'T GO AWAY AND HE HAD TO TELL JOAN

HE WANTED OUT - AND NOT IN A GAY WAY.

IT DIDN'T GO DOWN WELL, IN FACT JOAN THREATENED TO END IT ALL. GLENN, BEING A STAND-UP TYPE OF GUY COULDN'T LET HER DO THAT, SO HE FAKED HIS OWN DEATH. WHEN DEATH TURNED UP TO CLAIM GLENN'S BODY JOAN PLEADED WITH DEATH NOT TO TAKE HIM, GRABBED DEATH'S ARM AND FELL DEAD. WELL, SHE WAS SUICIDAL SO IT WAS COMING. DEATH DECIDES HE CAME FOR A BODY AND HE'S GOT ONE, A COLD, UNFEELING, TIRED LOOKING CORPSE FOR HIM TO TAKE TO THE UNDERWORLD - LIKE SUSAN SARANDON. GLENN, BEING THE CONSIDERATE SEXUAL DEVIANT HE IS, JUST ASKS DEATH FOR FIVE MINUTES ALONE WITH THE BODY. IT'S RUMOURED GLENN USED TO BE A NECROPHILIAC, UNTIL SOME ROTTEN BITCH SPLIT ON HIM.

GLENN, A FORMER U.S. NAVY ENSIGN, IS 61-YEARS OLD DESPITE BEING LISTED AS

THE SAME AGE AS PETER IN 'MEET THE QUAGMIRES'. IMAGINE IF MICHAEL J. FOX HAD COME BACK FROM THE FUTURE AND AGED REALLY BADLY. OH YEAH. GLENN STAYS YOUNG LOOKING VIA THE GIFT OF CARROTS. SO BUGS BUNNY, YOUR SECRET HAS BEEN RUMBLED.

DESPITE BEING A HEARTLESS SEX HOUND, GLENN DOES HAVE ONE SECRET DESIRE: LOIS. THIS MIGHT BE SACRILEGIOUS, BUT SURELY GLENN WOULD MAKE A BETTER LEAD IN FAMILY GUY THAN PETER? TWO WITTY, ATTRACTIVE, SEXUALLY ACTIVE PEOPLE COMING TOGETHER FOR THE SAKE OF COMEDY? LIKE MARIE AND FRANK ON 'EVERYBODY LOVES RAYMOND'? OH, HI PETER. WHAT WAS THAT FOR? I WAS JUST SAYING... PLEASE STOP PETER. PLEASE STOP. I'M BLEEDING, PUT DOWN THAT POKER PETER, VIOLENCE SOLVES NOTHING. JUST KISS ME PETER... KISS ME AND HOLD ME. AND MEAN NOTHING BY IT...

FUN FACTS

- ALTHOUGH OFTEN SEEN IN HIS UNIFORM AT AIRPORTS OR ON HIS WAY TO WORK, IT WAS NOT UNTIL THE SEASON FIVE EPISODE 'AIRPORT '07' THAT WE FIRST SAW QUAGMIRE PERFORMING HIS JOB AS A BOEING 767 CAPTAIN.

- THE ONE THING THAT REALLY DOESN'T AROUSE QUAGMIRE IS THE USE OF THE WORD 'RUBBISH' WHEN YOU SHOULD REALLY SAY 'GARBAGE'.

- THE NAME QUAGMIRE WAS COINED BY A COLLEGE FRIEND OF FAMILY GUY CREATOR SETH MACFARLANE. THE WORD MESHES SOFT SOIL WITH A SITUATION THAT IS DIFFICULT TO GET OUT OF - THINK OF GLENN'S LIFE AS SEXUAL QUICKSAND.

THE BROWNS MAY BE A THING OF THE PAST, LIKE JOHN TRAVOLTA'S WAIST, HAIRLINE AND TALENT, BUT THERE WAS A TIME CLEVELAND AND LORETTA HAD SOMETHING VERY, VERY SPECIAL.

BOTH PROUD AFRICAN AMERICANS, LORETTA AND CLEVELAND HAD A LOT IN COMMON: ALWAYS BETTING ON BLACK, NOT LIKING WHITE LITERATURE IN THEIR HOUSE AND (PARTICULARLY LORRETA) EXCEPTIONAL CRICKETERS. IT WAS, HOWEVER, OPPOSITES THAT ATTRACTED. HIM, A QUIET, PATIENT, GENTLE SOUL: 'I TOO HAVE FELT THE COLD FINGER OF INJUSTICE ON MY INSIDEY PARTS...' HER, A LOUDMOUTHED, JERRY SPRINGER-WANNABEE FATASS: 'SHUT UP AND PUT SOME MORE OF THAT SUGA' IN MY BOWL'. LORETTA WAS THE

LAW IN THE BROWN HOUSE AND ULTIMATELY HER FIRE BURNED JUST THAT LITTLE TOO BRIGHT. THIS RED-HOT WHIRLWINDY TORNADOEY HURRICANEY THING OF A WOMAN COULDN'T TAKE CLEVELAND'S COLDNESS AND, AS YOU MIGHT EXPECT, IN HER HOUR OF NEED, TURNED TO THE LOVING ARMS OF QUAGMIRE. CLEVELAND, DESPITE CONTINUING TO HARBOUR FEELINGS FOR HIS PARTNER, COULD NEVER RIDE UPON THE BLOATED GOOD SHIP LORETTA EVER AGAIN. ANOTHER STORY OF BOY-MEETS-GIRL, GIRL-WANTS-TO-EAT-BOY, GIRL-SLEEPS-WITH-QUAGMIRE.

CLEVELAND HAS DEBILITATING FOOT ODOUR AND A SLOW, PATIENT SPEECH PATTERN THANKS TO A FALLING TOTEM POLE THAT ENDED HIS CAREER AS A FAST-TALKING AUCTIONEER. BUT THAT DOESN'T MEAN HIS MIND HAS SLOWED UP AND HE'S QUICK TO PROMOTE THE POLITICAL AND CULTURAL PROFILE

OF HIS FELLOW AFRICAN AMERICANS. WHILE OUT TEN-PIN BOWLING HE TOLD JOE: "I MUST SAY, I DO FEEL A STRANGE SATISFACTION WATCHING THE BLACK BALL TOPPLE ALL THOSE SELF-RIGHTEOUS WHITE PINS." JOE: "CAN'T BLAME THEM FOR BEING SELF-RIGHTEOUS, THE BLACK BALL'S IN THEIR NEIGHBOURHOOD, UNINVITED." CLEVELAND: "THE BLACK BALL'S DONE NOTHING WRONG." JOE: "IF THE BLACK BALL'S INNOCENT, IT HAS NOTHING TO FEAR."

CLEVELAND'S SON, CLEVELAND JNR. IS A HYPERACTIVE BOY WHO SPEAKS QUICKLY AND HAS ATTENTION DEFICIT SYNDROME. YOU KNOW, WHEN YOU... HEY A COOKIE. NOW WHERE DID I LEAVE MY KEYS? HE DOESN'T APPEAR MUCH IN FAMILY GUY BUT A FATTER VERSION IS SET TO APPEAR IN THE CLEVELAND SHOW. HOW FAT IS HE? HE'S SO FAT, A CAR SWERVED TO MISS HIM AND RAN OUT GAS. OH YEAH.

FUN FACTS

- CLEVELAND WILL OFFICIALLY BE WRITTEN OUT OF FAMILY GUY DURING SEASON EIGHT BEFORE THE CLEVELAND SHOW IS BROADCAST. BUT HE'S NEVER FAR AWAY AND WILL RE-APPEAR FROM TIME TO TIME, LIKE HERPES.

- THE CLEVELAND SHOW WILL INCLUDE CLEVELAND'S NEW WIFE, DONNA. THERE'LL ALSO BE A COUPLE OF STEP-SIBLINGS FOR CLEVELAND JNR. DONNA'S 15-YEAR-OLD DAUGHTER, ROBERTA AND HER 5-YEAR-OLD SON, RALLO. KANYE WEST WILL PROVIDE THE VOICE FOR ONE OF CLEVELAND'S SON'S SOCCER RIVALS, KENNY WEST.

- MIKE HENRY, THE VOICE OF CLEVELAND, SAID THE INSPIRATION FOR CLEVELAND'S TONE WAS A GUY THAT HE MET WHO TOLD HIM HE HAD GRADUATED FROM THE UNIVERSITY OF MARYLAND. PEOPLE SAYING 'THE UNIVERSITY OF MERLIND' GOT TERRI.

FUNNY QUOTES

BRIAN

"I COULD TAKE MY SWEATER OFF TOO, BUT I THINK IT'S ATTACHED TO MY SKIN."

"IF DOGS AREN'T SUPPOSED TO EAT DENTAL FLOSS OUT OF THE TRASH, WHY DID THEY MAKE IT MINT FLAVOURED?"

"CHRIS YOU CAN'T JOIN THE ARMY! BESIDES, THE ARMY'S WEAK. NOW THE MARINES! THOSE ARE THE MEN YOU WANNA HAVE."

"OK CHRIS. NOW THAT WE HAVE PRACTICED KISSING AND CUDDLING, WE'LL PRACTICE EATING OUT... AT A FANCY RESTAURANT."

"I'VE SEEN THAT CRAPPY JULIA ROBERTS MOVIE FORTY-SEVEN TIMES. HAVE YOU SEEN THE LIPS ON THAT WOMAN? LIKE A BABOON'S ASS ON HER FACE."

"MY DAYS IN COLLEGE WERE SO EXCITING. THIS ONE TIME, THE NATIONAL GUARD CAME AND SHOT SOME OF MY FRIENDS."

PETER

"HEY LOIS, GIVE CHRIS A BREAK. I MEAN, NO TV? SO HE FAILED A CLASS, IT'S NOT LIKE HE FELT UP HIS COUSIN IN THE GARAGE THAT ONE TIME WHEN I WAS 19."

"THE DEEP SOUTH? ISN'T THAT THE PLACE WHERE THE BLACK GUYS ARE REALLY LAZY AND ALL THE WHITE GUYS ARE JUST AS LAZY BUT THEY'RE MAD AT THE BLACK GUY FOR BEING SO LAZY?

"I WALKED INTO THE KITCHEN AND SAT DOWN AT THE TABLE. I LOOKED WITH A GRIMACE AT THE QUESTIONABLE MEAL LOIS HAD PLACED IN FRONT OF ME. OF COURSE I'D NEVER TELL HER HOW DISGUSTED I WAS WITH HER COOKING, BUT SOMEHOW I THINK SHE KNEW. LOIS HAD ALWAYS BEEN FULL OF ENERGY AND LIFE, BUT LATELY I HAD BEGUN TO GROW MORE AWARE OF HER AGEING. THE BRIGHT, EXUBERANT EYE THAT I HAD FALLEN IN LOVE WITH WERE NOW BEGINNING TO GROW DULL AND LISTLESS WITH THE LONG FATIGUE OF A WEARY LIFE."

LOIS

PETER

"HERE'S TO OUR NEIGHBOURS. THEY MAY BE BLACK, HANDICAPPED, OR A HEARTLESS SEX HOUND. BUT IF IT WEREN'T FOR THEM, SOME SMELLY HAWAIIANS MIGHT MOVE IN."

"FOR MORE ABOUT FLATULENCE, YOU CAN VISIT MY ASS!"

"LOIS, IT'S TIME I JOINED THE RANKS OF GREAT MEN WITH BEARDS. WHY DO YOU THINK JESUS CHRIST WAS SO POPULAR? CAUSE, UH... CAUSE OF ALL THEM MAGIC TRICKS?"

"LOIS, BEFORE I FOUND THESE MOVIES, WOMEN ONLY MADE ME CRY THROUGH MY PENIS. NOW THEY MAKE ME CRY THROUGH MY EYES."

STEWIE

"NOTHING SAYS "OBEY ME" LIKE A BLOODY HEAD ON A FENCE POST!"

"GOD, ALL THIS WORK KEEPING PEOPLE FROM HAVING SEX, NOW I KNOW HOW THE CATHOLIC CHURCH FEELS!"

"MY MY, THE BIBLE, WHAT A THUMPING GOOD READ, LIONS EATING CHRISTIANS, PEOPLE NAILING EACH OTHER TO TWO BY FOURS. I'LL SAY, YOU WON'T FIND THAT IN WINNIE THE POOH."

"COME, ICE CREAM. COME TO MY MOUTH. HOW DARE YOU DISOBEY ME!"

"DID YOU HEAR THAT MEG? GUYS CAN MARRY OTHER GUYS NOW. SO...THIS IS AWKWARD, BUT I MEAN, IF THEY CAN DO THAT, THAT IS PRETTY MUCH IT FOR YOU, ISN'T IT? I MEAN YOU MAY AS WELL PACK IT IN. GAME OVER."

CHRIS

"I DON'T HAVE ANY MONEY SO I'M GOING TO HAVE TO PAY FOR THESE COMIC BOOKS WITH MY POOH."

THE GRIFFIN
FAMILY TREE

THE GRIFFIN FAMILY TREE IS A DRUNKEN, WILD AND UNWIELDY
BEAST THAT STINKS OF RUSSIAN CIGARETTES AND THROWS
ITS ROTTING APPLES AT PASSERS-BY WHILE SHOUTING 'YOU
WEREN'T THERE MAN! YOU DON'T KNOW WHAT IT WAS LIKE'. ITS
BRANCHES DART AND FURROW IN EVERY DANGEROUS DIRECTION
CRADLING IN THEM SOME OF THE SCARIEST PEOPLE YOU'RE
EVER LIKELY TO READ ABOUT OUTSIDE OF CHRISTIANS & GUNS
WEEKLY. HERE WE TAKE A LOOK FROM WHENCE THE GRIFFIN
SAPLINGS SPRUNG IN THIS INDISPENSABLE A TO U FAMILY TREE.

PETER'S SCOTTISH ANCESTOR, ANGUS
GRIFFIN, INVENTED THE FIRST RULES OF GOLF
WHICH DECREED THAT NO JEWS OR BLACKS
WOULD BE ALLOWED TO PLAY THE GAME.

PETER'S MEDIEVAL ANCESTOR, KING
ARTHUR GRIFFIN, AFTER BEING TOLD BY
GUINEVERE SHE WOULD MAKE LOVE TO
HIM IF HE LIFTED EXCALIBUR FROM THE
STONE ASKED: "WHAT IF I CAN JUST MOVE
IT AN INCH? WILL YOU TOUCH ME?"

D

DYLAN FLANNIGAN IS BRIAN'S HUMAN
SON TO TRACY FLANNIGAN. NOT MUCH
POINT TALKING ABOUT HIM, CAN'T
SEE HIM BEING AROUND FOR LONG
AFTER ALL THOSE LITTLE BITCHES
COMPLAINED SO MUCH ON THE NET.
SO HE WAS 13 WHEN BRIAN'S SEVEN?
BRIAN IS A TALKING DOG. THIS IS NOT A
DOCUMENTARY WE'RE WATCHING HERE.

e

PETER'S GREAT AUNT ELLA FITZGERALD
GRIFFIN WAS ACCOMPANIED ON PIANO
BY A YOUNG RAY CHARLES. HER SCAT
SOLO, HOWEVER, SHATTERED A GLASS
AND SENT SHARDS STRAIGHT INTO RAY
CHARLES'S EYES CAUSING HIS BLINDNESS.
AND JAMIE FOXX'S CAREER WAS BORN.

B

BERTRAM GRIFFIN IS THE UNBORN
SON OF PETER; A SPERM WHO
RESIDES IN THE DEEPEST RECESSES
OF PETER'S TWISTED TESTICLES
ONE OF PETER'S MORE DISTANT
RELATIVES, BLACK EYE GRIFFIN, WAS A
SILENT MOVIE ACTOR WHO RECEIVED A
BLACK EYE AT THE END OF EACH SKIT.

CHEESIE CHARLIE'S IS NO RELATION
- BUT A RESTAURANT THAT PETER
CLAIMS IS A TORTUE BUILDING.

G

GRANDPA GRIFFIN HELPED DESIGN BUGS
BUNNY. HE LOBBIED HARD FOR THE
NAME 'EPHRAIM THE RETARDED RABBIT'
BUT JUST LOST OUT TO EVERYONE
ELSE WORKING ON THE PROJECT. "OK.
WE'VE NARROWED IT DOWN TO TWO
POSSIBLE NAMES. ALL IN FAVOUR OF
BUGS BUNNY? AND ALL IN FAVOUR OF
EPHRAIM, THE RETARDED RABBIT?"...
"OH, YOU CAN ALL GO TO HELL..."

PETER'S LONG-DISTANT PAST CONTAINED A GREAT MAN. A MAN CALLED GRIFFIN PETERSON. A MAN WHO, AFTER BEING EXILED TO AMERICA BY KING STEWART, MADE THE NOW FAMOUS QUAHOGIAN ADDRESS: "I DECLARE THIS LAND, QUAHOG. WE'RE GONNA BUILD A NEW SETTLEMENT. WE'LL HAVE A HAPPY NEW LIFE, AND WE'LL HAVE EQUAL RIGHTS FOR ALL. EXCEPT BLACKS, ASIANS, HISPANICS, JEWS, GAYS, WOMEN, MUSLIMS, ERM, EVERYBODY WHO'S NOT A WHITE MAN. AND I MEAN WHITE WHITE, SO NO ITALIANS, NO POLISH. JUST PEOPLE FROM IRELAND, ENGLAND AND SCOTLAND. BUT FROM ONLY CERTAIN PARTS OF SCOTLAND AND IRELAND. JUST FULL BLOODED WHITES. NO, Y'KNOW WHAT? NOT EVEN WHITES. NOBODY GETS ANY RIGHTS. AHHHH ... AMERICA."

H

PETER'S GREAT GRANDFATHER, HUCK GRIFFIN, TRAVELLED THE MISSISSIPPI RIVER WITH HIS FRIEND 'N-WORD JIM'.

I

INDIANA JONES - NO RELATION, BUT FEATURES REGULARLY IN FAMILY GUY!

J

PETER'S GREAT, GREAT UNCLE, STAR WARS ANCESTOR, JABBA THE GRIFFIN, IS A BIG HUSKY MAN WHO ORDERS: "RAHSAAA NABBBBAA DOOARRR GOLA WOOKIEE NIPPLE PINCHY!"

K

PETER'S FAMOUS COUSIN KATHY GRIFFIN NEVER SHUTS UP. THEY'VE TRIED TO KEEP HER QUIET USING SEDATIVES BUT CHRIS DRANK FROM THE GLASS MEANT TO BE FOR KATHY.

L

LILLIAN MARIE 'LIL' PEWTERSCHMIDT WAS LOIS'S RETIRED GREAT AUNT.

SILAS PEWTERSCHMIDT'S DAUGHTER LOIS LAURA BUSH LYNN CHENEY PEWTERSCHMIDT STARTED AN INTER-RACIAL FAMILY IN SECRET WITH NATE GRIFFIN, AND LOOKS ALMOST IDENTICAL TO LOIS GRIFFIN.

LOIS' GREAT AUNT, MARGUERITE PEWTERSCHMIDT, DROPPED DEAD ONLY SECONDS AFTER APPEARING ON 'PETER, PETER CAVIAR EATER'. PETER FINDS OUT MARGUERITE IS COMING TO STAY FOR A WEEK.... "A WEEK! AW, JEEZ. NO, NO, NO, NO. PLEASE, GOD, KILL ME NOW. NO, NO, DAMN, DAMN, CRAP, DAMN IT TO HELL, SON OF A..." LOIS: "PETER!" PETER: "LOIS, SOMETIMES IT'S APPROPRIATE TO SWEAR." BAILIFF: "DO YOU SWEAR TO TELL THE WHOLE TRUTH, AND NOTHING BUT THE TRUTH, SO HELP YOU GOD?" PETER: "I DO. YOU BASTARD." LOIS: "I LOVE AUNT MARGUERITE. BECAUSE IF IT WASN'T FOR HER, I NEVER WOULD'VE MET YOU, PETER." (CUT TO YOUNGER LOIS AT THE POOL) LOIS: "AUNT MARGUERITE, HAVE YOU SEEN MY TOWEL?" AUNT MARGUERITE: "HAVE THE TOWEL BOY BRING YOU ANOTHER." LOIS: "I DON'T WANT TO BOTHER HIM." AUNT MARGUERITE: "NONSENSE, DEAR. YOU'RE A PEWTERSCHMIDT. TOWEL BOY!" PETER: "HI, MY NAME IS TOWEL. I HAVE A PETER FOR YOU. MY NAME IS PETER, AND I'LL BE YOUR NIPPLES...TOWEL BOY! AW, JEEZ."

PETER'S ANCIENT JEWISH ANCESTOR, MOSES GRIFFIN, WROTE THE TEN COMMANDMENTS, INCLUDING: "WHEN WE PASS A BILLBOARD, PLEASE DON'T READ IT OUT LOUD".

PETER'S GREAT, GREAT, GREAT, GREAT BLACK SLAVE GRANDFATHER ANCESTOR, NATHANIEL 'NATE' GRIFFIN WAS THE PEWTERSCHMIDT STABLE BOY. WHILE DUTIFULLY CALLING THEM 'MASSA', HE ALSO URINATED IN THEIR CEREAL AND HAD SEX WITH LOIS LAURA BUSH LYNNE CHENEY PEWTERSCHMIDT AND HER BEAUTIFUL SISTER.

WHILE IT UNLIKELY THAT STEWIE'S MARRIAGE TO OLIVIA GRIFFIN WAS MADE LEGAL (THE UNION WAS SANCTIFIED BY RUPERT WEARING A MINISTER'S COLLAR) SHE WAS, AT ONE TIME, THE MOST IMPORTANT PERSON IN STEWIE'S LIFE. BEFORE THAT THE BITCH STARTED HANGING AROUND WITH THREE DIAPER COMMERCIALS VICTOR. WELL THEY'RE DEAD NOW. DEAD IN THEIR LITTLE FLAMING CARDBOARD HOUSE. HA.
PETER'S GREAT GRANDFATHER, OSIAS GRIFFIN, WAS THE OWNER OF THE EIGHTH TELEPHONE EVER MADE. HIS TELEPHONE NUMBER WAS THREE. HOWEVER, HE ONCE RECEIVED A CALL FOR SEVEN. EASY TO MISS-DIAL.

THE DECEASED SON OF PETER AND LOIS, PETER GRIFFIN JR, WAS ACCIDENTALLY KILLED BY PETER IN 'THE JUICE IS LOOSE'. "I THOUGHT IF I SHOCK HIM ENOUGH I'D STOP CRYING. I WAS KINDA RIGHT."

PETER'S GREAT UNCLE AND BROTHER OF ADOLF HITLER, PETER HITLER, WAS ALWAYS INTERRUPTING ADOLF DOING HIS 'NAZI STUFF' BY GIVING FEEDBACK ON THIS RALLIES AND THE LIKE. OH, AND HE ACCIDENTALLY SHOT ADOLF AND WIFE EVA BRAUN WHILE PLAYING WITH A GUN – NOT WANTING TO GET CAUGHT, HE MADE IT LOOK LIKE THEY KILLED THEMSELVES. SASSY.

PONCE DE LEON GRIFFIN WAS PETER'S EXPLORER ANCESTOR WHO SEARCHED FOR THE FOUNTAIN OF YOUTH, FOUND IT, GOT IN AND CAME OUT WITH THE BODY OF A BABY AND THE HEAD OF A MAN; THE ONLY PART OF HIM THAT WASN'T SUBMERGED.

Q

PETER'S NEPHEW, QUARK GRIFFIN, IS A FERENGI. THE FERENGIS AND THEIR CULTURE ARE CHARACTERISED BY AN OBSESSION WITH PROFIT AND TRADE AND THEIR CONSTANT EFFORTS TO SWINDLE PEOPLE INTO BAD DEALS. IMAGINE ITALIANS, BUT WITH BIG EARS AND POOR TEETH, LIKE ITALIANS.

R

PETER'S BLACK COUSIN, RUFUS GRIFFIN, IS AN ACTOR WHO STARRED IN BLAXPLOITATION CLASSIC 'CADDYBLACK', 'BLACKDRAFT', 'BLACK TO THE FUTURE' AND, ERM, 'BLACK KRAMER VS. KRAMER'.

AN ANCESTOR OF THE PEWTERSCHMIDT FAMILY, SILAS PEWTERSCHMIDT LOOKS ALMOST IDENTICAL TO LOIS' FATHER, CARTER. SILAS WAS ONE OF THE FIRST TO COLONIZE AMERICA AND BARTERED WITH NATIVE AMERICANS BY HOLDING A KNIFE TO A BABY'S THROAT, SPARING ITS LIFE IN EXCHANGE FOR CORN.

STEWIE'S COUSIN, STEWIE CRUISE, APPEARS ON OPRAH AND REPEATEDLY ANNOUNCES THAT HE IS IN LOVE WITH KATIE HOLMES. AND THAT HE IS NOT GAY.

THADDEUS GRIFFIN, PETER'S EVIL TWIN BROTHER, COMES COMPLETE WITH WAXY MOUSTACHE AND CAPE, SHOWS UP AND WONDERS HOW IT WILL AFFECT HIS INHERITANCE.

PETER'S MOTHER, 85-YEAR-OLD THELMA GRIFFIN IS A COMMITTED SMOKER AND GAMBLER WHO LEFT HER HUSBAND BECAUSE HE COULDN'T SATISFY HER NEEDS. IN HER OWN WORDS, SHE: 'NEEDED SOMEONE TO CLEAR ALL THE BATS OUT OF MY PLUMBING'. THE GRIFFINS HAVE A ROCKET-POWERED ESCAPE POD IN THE SIDE OF THEIR HOME FOR A QUICK ESCAPE WHEN SHE VISITS.

PETER'S DISTANT RELATIVE, THOMAS GRIFFIN, REMAINS, ACCORDING TO PETER, ONE OF THE WORLD'S GREATEST PHILOSOPHERS. WHEN HIS WIFE ASKED HIM: 'THOMAS, WOULD YOU PLEASE GO LOOK FOR A JOB?' HE REPLIED: 'WHY?'

U

PETER'S GREAT, GREAT GRANDFATHER ANCESTOR, ULYSSES S. GRIFFIN, ENDED THE AMERICAN CIVIL WAR BY BEATING ROBERT E. LEE IN A BEER-DRINKING CONTEST.

PETER'S STONE AGE CAVEMAN ANCESTOR UR-PETER INVENTED THE WHEEL. WHEN HE COULDN'T SELL IT, HE PUT UR-LOIS, NEXT TO THE WHEEL WEARING A BRA AND PANTIES AND SOLD IT IMMEDIATELY IN A SCALPELESQUE INCISION THAT STRUCK RIGHT AT THE HEART OF THE ADVERTISING INDUSTRY'S OBJECTIFICATION OF WOMEN. MODERN ADVERTISING IS STILL RECOVERING FROM THAT DAGGER.

CRAZY CONNECTIONS

YOU KNOW SOMETHING? FAMILY GUY HAS MORE CONNECTIONS THAN KEANU REEVES IN 'THE MATRIX' IN THAT SCENE WHERE THE TUBES POP OUT OF HIS EYEHOLES, EAR HOLES, MOUTH HOLES AND ASSHOLES. WHEN HE FALLS OUT OF HIS CUTE LITTLE TUB INTO A GOOEY LAKE OF CRAP IT REMINDED ME OF THE TIME WE THREW THE BABY OUT WITH THE BATH WATER. STEWIE WASN'T HAPPY.

WHILE WE'RE THERE, REEVES SHOULD HAVE TAKEN THE BLUE PILL AND SAVED US ALL FROM THOSE SEQUELS. I MEAN, FOR GOD'S SAKE, YOU COULD HAVE PUT ALBERT EINSTEIN, ISAAC NEWTON AND CYNDI LAUPER'S BRAINS INTO A BLENDER, SHOOK IT UP, STUFFED IT INTO STEPHEN HAWKIN'S HEAD AND HE STILL COULDN'T HAVE TYPED OUT WHAT... WAS... GOING... ON...

HERE'S SOME WEIRD STUFF WE'RE CONNECTED TO...

PINBOARD

WILLIAM H. MACY ORIGINALLY AUDITIONED FOR THE ROLE OF BRIAN.

GLEN QUAGMIRE'S FACE IS MODELLED AFTER BOB HOPE.

STEWIE'S VOICE IS BASED ON REX HARRISON IN MY FAIR LADY.

IN 'NORTH BY NORTH QUAHOG', JESUS' LICENSE PLATE IS 'WWID', WHICH STANDS FOR 'WHAT WOULD I DO?'

LISA WILHOIT, THE VOICE OF CONNIE D'AMICO PLAYED A YOUNG JULIA ROBERTS IN THE FILM 'HOOK'.

IN THE 1987 MOVIE 'DRAGONARD', THE VOICE OF JOE SWANSON, PATRICK WARBURTON SUFFERED PLAYED A 17TH-CENTURY SLAVE ON A CARIBBEAN ISLAND THAT WAS LASHED FOR AN ASTONISHING THREE MINUTES AND 50 SECONDS.

LORI ALAN, THE VOICE OF DIANE SIMMONS, IS ALSO THE VOICE OF 'THE BOSS' ON VIDEOGAME 'METAL GEAR SOLID 3: SNAKE EATER'.

SETH MACFARLANE WAS THE VOICE OF JOHAN KRAUSS IN 'HELLBOY II'. KRAUSS IS MADE OF ECTOPLASM AND HAS NO PHYSICAL BODY – HE REQUIRES NEITHER SLEEP NOR FOOD.

ALEX BERNSTEIN, THE VOICE OF LOIS GRIFFIN, HAD A FAMOUS BUS DRIVER WHILE AT SCHOOL – ONE JOHN MALKOVICH.

FORMER BATMAN ADAM WEST, THE VOICE OF, ERM MAYOR ADAM WEST, CRIED FOR AN HOUR WHEN TIM BURTON FAILED TO CAST HIM IN THE FIRST MODERN 'BATMAN' MOVIE, INSTEAD OPTING FOR MICHAEL KEATON.

JAY MOHR, WHO DOES THE VOICE OF JOE PESCI ON THE SHOW, CAN DO THE BEST IMPRESSIONS OF SEAN PENN AND CHRISTOPHER WALKEN THAT YOU HAVE EVER HEARD. HE ALSO PLAYED 'BOB SUGAR' IN JERRY MAGUIRE. BOB SUGAR WAS THE PROTEGE WHO FIRED MAGUIRE THEN TOOK ALL HIS CLIENTS

SETH GREEN, WHO PROVIDES THE VOICE TO CHRIS GRIFFIN, AUDITIONED FOR THE AMERICAN BEAUTY ROLE THAT EVENTUALLY WENT TO WES BENTLEY AND JUST MISSED OUT ON THE ETERNAL SUNSHINE OF THE SPOTLESS MIND'S ROLE THAT WENT TO ELIJAH WOOD.

R&B STAR CHRISTINA MILIAN HAS CONFIRMED SHE WILL BE APPEARING IN AN EPISODE SET TO BE AIRED IN 2010.

QUAHOG TV

QUAHOG **5** NEWS

AUTO CUE

 "HI, I'M TOM TUCKER"

 "HI, I'M DIANE SIMMONS AND WELCOME TO CHANNEL 5 (WQHG)".

 "IN TONIGHT'S NEWS, LANDO GRIFFIN, A POPULAR STUDENT AT A LOCAL HIGH SCHOOL WAS KILLED LAST NIGHT WHEN HIS MOTORCYCLE CAREERED OFF DEAD MAN'S CURVE. POLICE WERE BAFFLED WHEN NO BODY WAS FOUND AT THE SCENE, BUT DECIDED IT WAS BEST NOT TO ASK QUESTIONS AND JUST LET EVERYONE GET ON WITH THEIR LIVES. DIANE."

 "TOM. THE MAN WHO HAS DONE MORE DRUGS THAN ANY OTHER HUMAN BEING ON THE PLANET WAS KILLED TODAY BY A PACK OF RABID DOGS HE THOUGHT HE SAW. TOM."

 "DIANE. COMING UP, OUR INVESTIGATIVE REPORT ON THE CLITORIS: 'NATURE'S RUBIK'S CUBE' AND OUR UPDATE ON A LOVEABLE LITTLE PIG THAT REFUSES TO EAT JEWS. BUT FIRST WE GO TO TRISHA TAKINAWA WHO IS ON THE STEPS OF QUAHOG TOWN HALL AND CONTINUES TO PLOUGH THROUGH THE TIRING CHARADE THAT OUR ELECTED OFFICIALS ACTUALLY CARE ABOUT THE PUBLIC OR HAVE SOMETHING MEANINGFUL TO SAY. TRISHA, GIVE IT TO US LONG TIME."

"TOM. THANK YOU, TOM. HERE COMES MAYOR ADAM WEST HIMSELF. MR. WEST, DO YOU HAVE ANY WORDS FOR OUR VIEWERS?

MAW "BOX, TOASTER, ALUMINIUM, MAPLE SYRUP... NO I TAKE THAT ONE BACK. I'M GONNA HOLD ONTO THAT ONE."

 "THANKS TRISHA. NOW WE GO TO A DIANE SIMMONS' DOUBLE-SPECIAL REPORT ON QUAHOG'S RECENT SPECIAL PEOPLE'S GAMES."

 "TOM, YOU FIND ME HERE AT WHAT IS A GREAT DAY TO BE ALIVE, ESPECIALLY IF YOU'RE ABLE-BODIED. TODAY WE'LL SEE SOME OF QUAHOG'S BRAVEST ATHLETES STRUGGLE VALIANTLY AGAINST GOD'S TWISTED DESIGNS. YOU'LL CHEER, YOU'LL CRY, YOU MIGHT EVEN GET A CHEAP LAUGH OR TWO. IN FACT, THERE'S THE DISTINCT POSSIBILITY THAT BY THE END OF THE DAY, WE'LL ALL BE GOING TO HELL."

 "ALREADY THERE, DIANE, AND NOW TIME FOR OLLIE WILLIAMS WITH THE BLACK-U-WEATHER FORECAST. OLLIE?"

 "IT GON RAIN!"

 "THANKS, OLLIE. IN LOCAL NEWS, A SEXY NEW TREND HAS EMERGED AT JAMES WOODS HIGH. DIANE."

 "THAT'S RIGHT, TOM. IT APPEARS THAT STUDENTS HAVE TAKEN TO HAVING EAR SEX IN LIEU OF TRADITIONAL INTERCOURSE."

 "OVER 200 REPORTS OF EAR SEX HAVE BEEN CONFIRMED SO FAR, PROMPTING A NEW SLOGAN: "ONCE YOU GO BLACK, YOU GO DEAF.""

 "IN OTHER NEWS, AFTER SEVERAL GRUELLING DAYS OF FRIGHTENING UNCERTAINTY, I FINALLY GET MY PERIOD."

 "WELL DIANE, I'M SURE YOU AND YOUR BROTHER MUST BE DEVASTATED BY THE LOSS OF THE TWO-HEADED OFFSPRING THAT MIGHT HAVE BEEN."

 "THANKS TOM. AND FINALLY, TOM'S DARED ME TO DO THE NEWS TOPLESS. I'VE GOT THE GOODS BUT DO I HAVE THE GUTS? FIND OUT AT 11."

 "THAT'S BREAKING NEWS AND MAYBE DIANE'S BOOBS LATER TONIGHT."

MEET THE TEAM

QUAHOG 5 NEWS

THOMAS 'TOM' TUCKER

A MAN AS COMMITTED TO RATINGS AS JACQUELINE STALLONE IS TO SCARING CHILDREN, LADIES AND GENTLEMEN, IF WE SAY TOM TUCKER IS A NEWSMAN, YOU GOT TO AGREE. SOME SAY HE'S ARROGANT, OTHERS CONCEITED, OTHERS SMUG, BUT THEY ALL AGREE: HE'S ARROGANT, SMUG AND CONCEITED. TUCKER IS MARRIED TO STACY, HIS SECOND WIFE, AND HAS A SON, JAKE, FROM HIS FIRST MARRIAGE, A BOY WHO HAS NEVER LEARNED HOW TO WIPE BECAUSE HE DOES NOT HAVE A BOTTOM. TUCKER HATES HIS WIFE AND IS SO ASHAMED OF HIS SON JAKE'S (PREVIOUSLY) UPSIDE DOWN FACE THAT HIS ENTIRE HOUSE IS FULL OF PICTURES OF HIM, INCLUDING ONE OF HIM IN A WEDDING DRESS.

DIANE SIMMONS

TOM'S CO-ANCHOR, DIANE'S FULL NAME IS DIANE SEIDELMAN. SHE COULD BE JEWISH BUT GOT RID OF THE DEFECT TO ENTER THE WORLD OF MEDIA, LIKE WYNONA RYDERKATZ, ELI ROTHBERG OR JOAQUIN PHOENIXWITZ. SIMMONS IS A REPEATED BREAST FLASHER AND RELAXES IN HER SPARE TIME BY HIRING MALE PROSTITUTES. A FORMER HUSBAND COMMITTED SUICIDE BY BLOWING HIS BRAINS OUT. SHE ADMITS TO BEING RACIST AGAINST BLACK PEOPLE.

TRICIA TAKANAWA

IF IT'S A DIRTY JOB, QUAHOG 5'S ASIAN CORRESPONDENT HAS TO DO IT. SHE HAS HUMPED DAVID BOWIE'S LEG WHILE PROMISING 'I MAKE YOU FISH BOWL SOUP!', VOMITED WHILE COVERING A FLU EPIDEMIC, HAD ANONYMOUS SEX WITH A POSSIBLY-ON-DRUGS QUAGMIRE AND DURING 'DA BOOM' IS GRILLED AND EATEN BY TOM AND DIANE. IT IS RUMOURED THAT CONNIE CHUNG OF CBS SHUFFLES NERVOUSLY EVERY TIME TRICIA COMES ON SCREEN.

OLLIE WILLIAMS

QUAHOG 5'S BLACK METEOROLOGIST. HIS FORECASTS ARE LOUD, QUICK, CONCISE AND TO THE POINT – LIKE A MIKE TYSON ORGASM. PEEL BACK HIS MASK AND YOU'LL FIND A ROTTING PUMPKIN WHERE HIS HEAD SHOULD BE, SCRAPE THAT BACK AND YOU'LL FIND ANOTHER OLLIE WILLIAMS WHO IS EXTREMELY COMPUTER SAVVY. END OF LINE.

GREG THE WEATHER MIME

OLLIE'S COLLEAGUE ON THE CHANNEL 5 WEATHER TEAM MIMES THE QUAHOG WEATHER WHICH IS, IN TURN, INTERPRETED AND TRANSLATED BY TOM. GREG'S MIME WAS ONCE MISTAKEN FOR SIGNALLING THAT PARENTS WILL THROW FAECES AT THEIR CHILDREN FROM THE ROOFTOPS WHILE HE WAS SIMPLY SIGNING THAT IT WAS ABOUT TO RAIN. EASY MISTAKE TO MAKE, TOM.

MARIA JIMINEZ

A FLEETING MEMBER OF THE CHANNEL 5 NEWS TEAM, JIMINEZ HAS APPEARED ONLY ONCE, IN 'ONE IF BY CLAM, TWO IF BY SEA' WHERE SHE REPORTS ON PETER'S ARREST FOR ARSON. SHE HAS ONLY BEEN FLEETINGLY USED ON FAMILY GUY BECAUSE RESEARCH BY THE SHOW'S MARKETING AND DEMOGRAPHIC CONSULTANCY SHOWS 37.68% OF NON-HISPANIC AUDIENCES TO BE 'THREATENED AND UNCOMFORTABLE' WITH AN ARTICULATE HISPANIC. ALSO, TOM CAN'T PRONOUNCE HER NAME BECAUSE A 'J' SHOULD SOUND LIKE A 'J', NOT A FREAKIN' 'H'.

THE FAMILY GUY

SUPPORTING CAST

OH HEYYYYYY... BRUCE HERE. YOU KNOW, Y'ALL WELCOME TO MY LITTLE OL' PAGES ABOUT ME AND MY LITTLE 'OL FRIENDS. YOU KNOW, BIG STRONG PETER AND HIS SEXY FAMILY MIGHT BE TELLING YOU THAT FAMILY GUY IS ALL ABOUT THEM, AND OKAY, THEY'RE RIIIIIGHT. BUT YOU KNOW, THERE ARE SOME OTHER FOLKS WHO LIVE IN QUAHOG THAT YOU MIGHT WANT TO GET TO KNOW A LITTLE BETTER. I'M SORRY, I'M A LITTLE JITTERY. A LITTLE EXCITED 'CAUSE I MET SOMEBODY TODAY! SOMEONE IN THE VIDEO STORE! SOMEONE WHO LIKES THE SAME KINDA JEFF BRIDGES FILMS I DO! OH AND THE ADVENTURE BEGINS AGAIN!

LET ME INTRODUCE MASELF AGAIN, I'M BRUCE. YOU CAN CALL ME BRUCIE. I'M A PERFORMANCE ARTIST AND USED TO WORK IN THE HORROR NOVELTY SHOP BEFORE TEACHING A CPR COURSE AT JAMES WOODS REGIONAL HIGH SCHOOL. YOU COULD SAY I WENT FROM STOPPING HEARTS TO STARTING THEM UP AGAIN! OH STAWP! I ALSO PLAYED A MEDIUM IN 'PETERGEIST' WHEN EVERYONE KNOWS I'M AN EXTRA LARGE.

THIS IS MY FRIEND ANGELA. ANGELA IS HEAD OF THE SHIPPING DEPARTMENT OF THE PAWTUCKET BREWERY AND PETER'S SUPERVISOR. I THINK SHE MAY BE A LESBIAN, AND I'M ALL FOR THAT, SISTER. WHEN PETER FOUND OUT ANGELA WAS AN ANIMAL LOVER HE ORGANISED A COCKFIGHT IN HER HOUSE! NOW WHY DIDN'T HE COME OVER TO MA PLACE?

ON THE SUBJECT OF PEOPLE WHO HATE PETER, THERE'S ERNIE THE CHICKEN! HEY, ERNIE! ERNIE AND PETER HAVE NOT STOPPED FIGHTING SINCE PETER ACCIDENTLY PUNCHED HIM WHILE A TEENAGER AT THE COUNTRY CLUB DANCE. SINCE THEN, ERNIE AND PETER HAVE ENDURED MORE SELF-INFLICTED PAIN THAN WHITNEY HOUSTON'S NOSTRILS, FIGHTING ON TOP OF A MOVING TRUCK, HANGING OFF A HELICOPTER AND AN OUT OF CONTROL FERRIS WHEEL. OOH, THE FUN OF THE FAIR!

IT'S NOT JUST PETER WHO HAS A NEMESIS. CHRIS' EVIL FOE IS EVIL MONKEY, AN ANGRY FELLA WHO IS TOTALLY COMMITTED TO SCARING PETER. DO YOU KNOW, EVIL MONKEY ONCE BROKE DOWN IN TEARS, BECAUSE CHRIS LEFT SPOONER STREET? HE REALLY LOVES TO SCARE THAT BOY. MEG'S EVIL MONKEY IS CONNIE DIMICO, THE MOST POPULAR GIRL AT JAMES WOODS HIGH AND CAPTAIN OF THE CHEERLEADING SQUAD. SHE HAS DATED THREE OF THE GRIFFINS, STEWIE IN 'MCSTROKE', PETER IN 'LET'S GO TO THE HOP', AND CHRIS IN 'STEW-ROIDS'. SHE IS SO SKANKY SHE MAKES LINDSAY LOHAN LOOK LIKE PRINCESS STEPHANIE OF MONACO.

OH, AND DON'T FORGET GREASED UP DEAF GUY. HE'D BE SUCH A CATCH. OOOOOH, LISTEN TO ME. GREASED UP DEAF GUY FIRST APPEARED AT PETER'S PICNIC WHERE HE WAS RELEASED FROM A CAGE AND SHOUTED: "YOU'RE NEVER GONNA CATCH ME! YOU'RE WASTING YOUR TIME! FORGET ABOUT IT! GO DO SOMETHING ELSE! SEE YOU NEXT YEAR!" IN A HIGH-PITCHED VOICE BEFORE RUNNING OFF INTO THE FOREST. HE WAS FUNNY AND CUTE. LIKE THE NEGATIVE POLAROID OF SETH ROGEN.

I like The Sauce

SEAMUS? HE'S A SALTY SEADOG WITH WOOD FOR ARMS AND LEGS AND JUST ONE WITH WHICH TO FIGHT PETER PAN, NO SORRY THAT'S SEXY DR. HOOK. SEAMUS IS A SUPERSTITIOUS LITTLE MITE WHO, BETWEEN WARNING OTHERS ABOUT IMPENDING DOOM, HAS HIS OWN TELEVISION TALK SHOW. SEAMUS HAS BEEN ASKED ABOUT HIS WOODY DISORDER AND CONFIRMS THAT IT'S BECAUSE HIS FATHER WAS A 'TREE'.

YOU KNOW, SEAMUS IS ALWAYS UP FOR A BIT OF FISTICUFFS BUT THAT'S NOTHING COMPARED TO PADDY TANNIGER, THE CADDY MANAGER AT QUAHOG GOLF COURSE (AND LATER ON BRIAN'S BOSS IN A CAR SALESROOM). HE'S A SHORT, ANNOYING MAN WHO, WHENEVER HE STATES A FACT, FOLLOWS IT UP WITH, "BIG WHOOP, WANNA FIGHT ABOUT IT? I'M PADDY TANNIGER, THE CADDY MANAGER – YEAH IT RHYMES, BIG WHOOP, WANNA FIGHT ABOUT IT?!" DO YOU KNOW THOSE NAUGHTY WRITERS WROTE HIM OUT OF THE SERIES BECAUSE THEY DIDN'T LIKE HIM? I WOULD LIKE TO WRITE THAT BITCH JULIET OUT OF ROMEO AND JULIET.

I'D NEED A NICE BRITISH ACCENT THOUGH, LIKE THAT LOVELY NIGEL PINCHLEY, HE USED TO OWN THE DRUNKEN CLAM WHEN IT WAS KNOWN AS THE CLAM'S HEAD PUB BUT HE BURNED IT DOWN FOR THE INSURANCE MONEY. HE WAS HUNG FOR INSURANCE FRAUD BACK IN BRITAIN. THOSE CRAZY BRITS AND THEIR MEDIEVAL TORTURE, THEY'RE FUNNY.

BUT I LIKE A MORE PROFESSIONAL MAN, LIKE DR. HARTMAN. HE MAY WELL BE INCOMPETENT, BUT THOSE STERILE, RUBBER-GLOVED HANDS ARE SO SEXY. DR. HARTMAN WAS ONCE FIRED FOR DOING A PROSTATE EXAM ON PETER. PETER ACCUSED DR. HARTMAN OF RAPING HIM, AND HE'D ALREADY ABUSED CLEVELAND, QUAGMIRE (I WAS VIOLATED TOO. I ONLY WENT IN THERE FOR A GUINEA PIG REMOVAL) AND JOE (I SCRUBBED AND I SCRUBBED BUT DAMN IT, THEY DON'T MAKE WATER HOT ENOUGH!). BUT HE WAS JUST FLIRTIN'.

THOSE BRITS ALSO LIKE A DRINK, AND A FIGHT, SO THEY'D NEED A LITTLE PAWTUCKET PAT IN THEIR TANKS. YOU KNOW PAT LOOKS AN AWFUL LOT LIKE WILLY WONKA, HIS FACTORY IS RUN BY CHUMBAWUMBAS AND HE HELD A CONTEST FOR FOUR LUCKY PEOPLE TO FIND A SILVER SCROLL AND WIN A TOUR OF HIS FACTORY. FAMILY GUY WRITERS WERE GOING TO MAKE SURE GRANDPA BUCKET STARRED IN THE SHOW BUT HIS LIMBS WERE STUCK TO HIS BEDCLOTHES BY HIS OWN URINE. UNLUCKY!

BUT YOU KNOW WHO'S EVEN SEXIER THAN AN OLD MAN WHO STINKS OF HIS OWN PEE, IT'S GOT TO BE MAYOR WEST. DON'T YOU THINK HE WOULD MAKE A GREAT SUPERHERO? I DO. A GREAT BIG SEXY SPIDERMAN. HE'S GOT IT ALL: INTENSE, SOFT SPOKEN AND BIG AND STRONG AND A LITTE UNHINGED, LIKE WHEN MEG ASKED: "EXCUSE ME, MAYOR WEST?", HE RESPONDED: "HOW DO YOU KNOW MY LANGUAGE?!" OR WHEN HE SAW WATER GOING DOWN HIS DRAIN: "MY GOD! SOMEONE'S STEALING MY WATER! THE WATER PLANTS, THEY HIT WHEN YOU LEAST EXPECT IT. SHOW YOURSELVES, COWARDS! I'VE SPENT $1,000 OF THE TAX PAYERS' MONEY TRYING TO FIND THESE THIEVES AND I'LL SPEND $1,000,000 IF THAT'S WHAT IT TAKES!" HE'S A PRETTY DERANGED, DANGEROUS, SCREWED UP GUY, BUT I'D FEEL AS SAFE IN HIS ARMS AS THE CITY DOES IN HIS CARE.

SO THAT'S A FEW OF THE FOLKS IN FAMILY GUY. WE'RE A BUNCH WHO LIKE A GOOD TIME. I LIKE A GOOD TIME, LIKE WHEN I WORKED ON 911 CALL CENTRE? A WOMAN CALLED: "I THINK THERE'S SOMEONE IN MY HOUSE." I TOLD HER: "OH, I ENVY THAT. I LIVE ALONE. NOBODY EVER COMES OVER MY HOUSE." SHE SHOUTED: "NO! I MEAN THERE'S SOMEBODY IN MY HOUSE RIGHT

NOW!" I TOLD HER AGAIN: "WELL, MAYBE YOU'LL WANT TO PUT OUT SOME SNACKS OR SOMETHING. DOESN'T HAVE TO BE NOTHING FANCY. YOU CAN EVEN JUST OPEN UP A BOX OF WHEAT THINS AND POUR SOME IN A BOWL. MULTI-GRAIN'S ALWAYS GOOD." "OH MY GOD! THEY'RE COMING UP THE STAIRS!" I SAID: "OH, YOU'RE GOING TO HAVE TO CLOSE THAT BEDROOM DOOR IF YOUR BED'S NOT MADE. MAYBE, PERHAPS YOU COULD PUT ON A VIDEO LATER AND SNEAK UPSTAIRS TO MAKE THAT BED." "AHH!" "OH OH, LOOKS LIKE THEY SAW THAT BEDROOM." YOU SEE, WE'RE A FUN BUNCH. COME DOWN AND SEE US SOON, YOU HEAR?

HERBERT
& JESSE

YOU KNOW, I THINK WE CAN ALL AGREE THAT EVERY NEIGHBOURHOOD NEEDS A FRIENDLY OLD CROSS-DRESSING PAEDOPHILE WHO, BEFORE GENTLY HUMMING HIMSELF TO SLEEP WITH A RENDITION OF BACKSTREET BOYS' "I WANT IT THAT WAY", PRAYS TO BEELZEBUB SO CHRIS GRIFFIN AND A COPY OF 'WHAT BOY' MAGAZINE ACCOMPANIES EVERY SWEET SUNRISE. WELL, SPOONER STREET IS NO EXCEPTION.

HERBERT IS A DIRTY OLD MAN AND WITH A DIRTY OLD MIND AND DIRTY OLD DOG, JESSE, HE 'DON'T MEAN NO HARM' BUT LOOK BEYOND HERBERT'S SOFT, EFFEMINATE, WISPY VOICE, SOILED BLUE ROBE, ZIMMER FRAME AND DILAPIDATED BODY AND YOU'LL FIND A MIND SO CUNNING AND DECEPTIVE IT COULD PASS SANDRA BULLOCK OFF AS AN ACTRESS.

IN FACT, HERBERT'S TRIED EVERY TRICK IN HIS WELL-THUMBED BOOK TO ENTICE CHRIS FOR AN AFTERNOON'S DELIGHT.

COMPLIMENTS

"HMMM.... THAT'S A NICE MUSCLEY THROWING ARM YOU GOT THERE..."

BRIBES

"I'VE GOT A TIP FOR YA' HERE IN MY POCKET, WHY DON'T REACH IN HERE YOURSELF AND FISH IT OUT?"

"YOU NEED TO COME ON DOWN TO THE CELLAR, SON. I'VE GOT A WHOLE FREEZER FULL OF POPSICLES"

THREATS

"YOU'RE STARTIN' TO PEE ME OFF, YOU PIGGLY SON OF A BITCH! (PAUSE) CALL ME!"

CONCILIATION

"BOYS, BOYS, WE CAN SETTLE THIS LIKE REASONABLE AND SEXY TEENAGERS. WHOEVER CAN SWALLOW THE MOST TYLENOL PM WINS!"

CONCERN

"YOU DON'T WANNA HURT YOURSELF DANCING; MAKE SURE YOU STRETCH OUT THOSE CREAMY HAMSTRINGS."

BUT IF ALL ELSE FAILS, AT LEAST HERBERT KNOWS, LIKE PRINCESS LEIA, THERE IS AT LEAST ONE MORE IN THE FAMILY WITH THE FORCE, STEWIE. REMEMBER WHEN STEWIE STOOD IN FOR CHRIS ON HIS PAPER ROUND? "OH, OSHKOSH B'GOSH, IT'S A

BRAND NEW PAPERBOY! THAT'S A MIGHTY FULL SACK YOU'RE CARRYING." STEWIE RETORTED: "P**S OFF, YOU PERVERTED OLD FREAK!" "OH-HO, WE GOT A FIGHTER," CONFIRMED THE OLD MAN. NO. THERE IS ANOTHER.

JESSE

EVERY SUPERHERO NEEDS A SIDEKICK. JESSE, HERBERT'S DOG, IS PARALYZED FROM THE WAIST DOWN, AND SHARES IDENTICAL HUMS AND DISABILITIES TO THE GREAT MAN. THOUGH WHY IS HE CALLED A SIDEKICK? HE CAN'T KICK AND WOULDN'T FEEL ONE. LET'S KICK HIM. KICK, KICK, KICK THE DOG. KICK, KICK, KICK THE DOG.

FACTS ABOUT HERBERT

HERBERT WAS DREAMT UP BY MIKE HENRY WHO WOULD, IN A DISAPPROVING MANNER, DO HIS VOICE EVERY TIME THE WRITERS HAD TROUBLE COMING UP WITH NEW IDEAS FOR EPISODES.

HERBERT WAS BASED ON A GROUP OF RETIRED OLD MEN WHO HENRY PUSHED GROCERIES WITH WHILE AT HIGH SCHOOL, ONE OF WHOM HAD A WHISTLEY VOICE.

IN 'PETERGEIST', HERBERT SAVES CHRIS FROM THE EVIL TREE, 'SKINNYBRITCHES', IN A SCENE REMINISCENT OF GANDALF V BALROG IN LORD OF THE RINGS. "HEY SKINNYBRITCHES, THAT THERE IS MY MAN, WHY DON'T YOU PICK ON SOMEONE YOUR OWN SIZE?" IN A SCENE CUT FOR TIME, THE TWO CLIMB OUT OF THE HOLE AND HERBERT ASKS: "ARE YOU A GIVING TREE OR RECEIVING TREE?"

HERBERT WAS ORIGINALLY GOING TO BE A CREEPY SCHOOL BUS DRIVER THAT CHRIS WAS AFRAID TO GO NEAR, OR AN ICE CREAM MAN.

Herbert

IT'S DIFFICULT TO WRITE ABOUT PETER'S COLLEAGUES, HE'S HAD MORE JOBS THAN RON JEREMY. HOWEVER, HIS TWO MAIN RESTING PLACES, AND WE MEAN THAT QUITE LITERALLY FOLKS, HAVE BEEN THE HAPPY-GO-LUCKY TOY FACTORY AND THE PAWTUCKET BREWERY.

MEET THE COLLEAGUES

THE HAPPY-GO-LUCKY FACTORY IS OWNED BY MR. WEED. FOR A SHORT PERIOD IT WAS BOUGHT OUT BY THE EL DORADO CIGARETTE COMPANY, WHO IMMEDIATELY STARTED MAKING TOYS TO PROMOTE UNDER-AGE SMOKING. NOTHING WRONG WITH THAT YOU MIGHT THINK, BUT PETER WENT TO CONFRONT THE MANAGEMENT BECAUSE HE'S A FAMILY GUY WHOSE PRINCIPLES CANNOT BE BOUGHT. NOT AT ANY PRICE. BECAUSE IF YOU DON'T HAVE PRINCIPLES, WHAT DO YOU HAVE? THAT'S RIGHT, NOTHING.

THE EL DORADO BOARD BRIBED PETER BY MAKING HIM PRESIDENT, GIVING HIS HOUSE A MICRO-THIN COATING OF TEFLON ON THE INSIDE TO MAKE IT EASY

CLEAN, APPOINTING MARTHA STEWART AS A HOUSEKEEPER AND HIRING AN UGLY GIRL TO STAND NEXT TO MEG TO MAKE HER PRETTIER. THAT'S PETER, A MAN OF CAST IRON PRINCIPLES.

JONATHAN WEED (DECEASED)

PETER'S BOSS AT HAPPY-GO-LUCKY AND DESCRIBED BY HIS EMPLOYEES AS AN 'EFFEMINATE WEIRDO'.

WHILE WORKING AT HAPPY-GO-LUCKY, PETER HAD A LONG AND SEXY RELATIONSHIP WORKING UNDER MR. WEED. ONE TIME, HE ASKED JOE TO APPEAR FOR HAPPY-GO-LUCKY IN THE BASEBALL GAME AGAINST PAWTUCKET JOKE & NOVELTIES.

MR. WEED: "IT'S NICE THAT YOUR FAMILY IS HERE, PETER. IF YOUR RINGER DOESN'T ARRIVE SOON, YOU CAN SPEND EVERY DAY WITH THEM- AT HOME." PETER: "HE'LL BE HERE, MR. WEED. YOU SHOULD SEE THIS GUY IN ACTION. HE CAN HIT, HE CAN THROW..." JOE: "PETER!" MR. WEED: "WHAT'S HE DOING IN A WHEELCHAIR?" PETER: "HOLY CRIP, HE'S A CRAPPLE!" MR. WEED: "PETER, OUR NEW SECRET WEAPON IS THIS VERY ATTRACTIVE PARAPLEGIC?" ANOTHER TIME, PETER FELL ASLEEP ON THE JOB. PETER CLAIMED: "THERE'S A BUG IN MY EYE AND I'M TRYING TO SUFFOCATE HIM." MR. WEED: "PETER, I LIKE YOU. BUT I NEED YOU TO BE MORE THAN JUST EYE CANDY AROUND HERE."

IT'S NOT THAT PETER DOESN'T WANT TO CLIMB THE GREASY CORPORATE POLE. IT'S JUST THAT HE CAN'T QUITE GET A DECENT HOLD: PETER: "MR. WEED, DISTINGUISHED MEMBERS OF THE BOARD, MAY I PRESENT THIS YEAR'S HOTTEST TOY...MR. ZUCCHINI HEAD. HE'S GOT STUPID COOL HIP-HOP STYLE WITH HIS LITTLE HAT AND HIS DOC MARTENS." MR. WEED: "THANK YOU, PETER, THAT'S ENOUGH." PETER: "WAIT, WAIT, WAIT. THIS IS THE BEST PART! HE DANCES!" DIRECTOR ONE: "I'VE SEEN ENOUGH." DIRECTOR TWO: "INAPPROPRIATE." DIRECTOR THREE: "I HAVEN'T HAD SEX IN FOUR YEARS." MR. WEED: "GENTLEMEN, I APOLOGIZE FOR WASTING YOUR TIME. PETER IS AN ADEQUATE ASSEMBLY-LINE WORKER BUT YOU'LL BE HAPPY TO KNOW OUR COMPANY DOES NOT PAY HIM TO THINK."

ANOTHER TIME, PETER, INVITED MR. WEED ROUND FOR DINNER. PETER: "I HOPE THAT THING DOESN'T HAPPEN WHERE I GET NERVOUS AND I CAN'T CONTROL OF THE VOLUME OF MY VOICE." MR. WEED: "HELLO, PETER." "HOW ARE YOU?" PETER: [YELLING] FINE! [QUIETLY] PLEASE COME IN." DURING DINNER IT WENT QUITE WELL: MR. WEED: "MMM! WHO WOULD THINK A WOMAN WITH SUCH BEAUTY WOULD HAVE THE CULINARY SKILLS OF EMERIL LAGASSE?" LOIS: "OH, WELL THANK YOU. BAM! PETER, DON'T YOU HAVE SOMETHING TO SAY TO MR. WEED?" PETER: "OH, YEAH. MR. WEED, I DON'T CARE WHAT THE GUYS AT WORK SAY. I NEVER THOUGHT YOU WERE AN EFFEMINATE WEIRDO." BRIAN: "SO, WHAT KIND OF A NAME IS "WEED"? MR. WEED: "THEY GAVE IT TO MY GRANDFATHER ON ELLIS ISLAND. OUR REAL NAME WAS BERMUDAGRASS. PETER, BEING HERE WITH YOUR WONDERFUL FAMILY, YOUR BEAUTIFUL HOME AND YOUR FUNNY TALKING DOG, WELL, I'M IMPRESSED.

IN FACT, STARTING MONDAY, I WOULD LIKE TO PROMOTE YOU TO HEAD OF TOY DEVELOPMENT." PETER: "HOLY CRAP! AH, THANKS, MR. WEED!"

OKAY, SO HE LATER DIED AFTER CHOKING TO DEATH ON A ROLL BUT BY THEN PETER HAD WON HIM ROUND AND THAT'S THE MAIN THING. AFTER HIS FUNERAL, MR. WEED CONFIRMED 'THE HAPPY-GO-LUCKY TOY FACTORY SHALL BE TORN DOWN TO MAKE WAY FOR THE HAPPY-GO-LUCKY TERMINAL DISEASE INSTITUTE.' ACCORDING TO THE QUAHOG 5 NEWS, THE DINNER ROLL IS NOW SERVING DOUBLE LIFE IMPRISONMENT, WITHOUT PAROLE.

PASQUAL & SANTOS

PORTUGUESE IMMIGRANTS WHO WORKED AS FISHERMEN WITH PETER. ONE WAS A CARDIOLOGIST IN PORTUGAL BUT FLED DUE TO A CRAZY SORCERER BEING AFTER THE PAIR.

THERE AIN'T NOTHING PETER DON'T KNOW ABOUT FISH, ESPECIALLY GOLDFISH, AND HOW TO COOK THEM. ANYWAY, LIKE I WAS SAYIN', GOLDFISH IS THE FRUIT OF THE SEA. YOU CAN BARBECUE IT, BOIL IT, BROIL IT, BAKE IT, AND SAUTE IT. DEY'S UH, GOLDFISH-KABOBS, GOLDFISH CREOLE, AND GOLDFISH GUMBO. PAN FRIED, DEEP FRIED, STIR-FRIED. THERE'S PINEAPPLE GOLDFISH, LEMON GOLDFISH, COCONUT GOLDFISH, PEPPER GOLDFISH, GOLDFISH SOUP, GOLDFISH STEW, GOLDFISH SALAD, GOLDFISH AND POTATOES, GOLDFISH BURGER, GOLDFISH SANDWICH...

OPIE

ENJOYS BITING FINGERS AND SHOVING A PENCIL INTO HIS BRAIN BY INSERTING IT INTO HIS EAR AND REPEATEDLY POUNDING HIS HEAD ON A DESK.

ANGELA

PETER'S SUPERVISOR, IN CHARGE OF THE SHIPPING DEPARTMENT. REPEATEDLY AWARDS OPIE AS EMPLOYEE OF THE MONTH AND PROMOTES HIM.

WHICH TAKES PETER TO THE PAWTUCKET BREWERY, HOME OF PETER'S FAVOURITE BEER.

AT THE PAWTUCKET BREWERY, HE REPEATEDLY GETS UNDER THE SKIN OF UBER-LESBIAN ANGELA AND IS REGULARLY OUTPERFORMED BY EMPLOYEE OF THE MONTH, OPIE. THIS IS EVEN HARDER TO BARE WHEN YOU CONSIDER THAT OPIE WEARS ODD SHOES, HAS DONALD PLEASANCE EYES AND HAIRCUT FROM VANILLA ICE'S NEW HAIR SALON: 'HAIR APPARENT' AND WHOSE MAIN CONTRIBUTION IS TO JOLT AROUND MADLY WHILE YELLING 'WABLU'. EVEN SO, IT'S UNDERSTANDABLE THAT PETER FAILS TO LIFT THAT EMPLOYEE OF THE MONTH TROPHY. HE CAN BE A LITTLE WORKSHY: PETER (LEAVING A MESSAGE FOR MR. WEED): "MR. WEED? THIS IS PETER GRIFFIN. I WILL NOT BE COMING TO WORK TODAY. I WAS IN A TERRIBLE PLANE CRASH. MY ENTIRE FAMILY WAS KILLED AND I AM A VEGETABLE."

FOUAD

QUICK TO EXPLAIN AND TO UNDERSTAND SARCASM OR IRONY "OHOHOHO! EES FUNNY BEE-CUZ..."

REAL LIFE CHARACTERS

FROM AMERICAN FOOTBALL BROADCASTER PAT SUMMERALL ON SEASON ONE OPENER 'DEATH HAS A SHADOW' RIGHT THROUGH TO DOOGIE HOWSER, M.D. NEIL PATRICK HARRIS ON SEASON SEVEN FINALE 'PETER'S PROGRESS', FAMOUS NAMES HAVE ROUTINELY QUEUED UP TO HUMILIATE THEMSELVES, THEIR FRIENDS AND THEIR FAMILIES IN A VAINGLORIOUS ATTEMPT TO SHOW THAT THEY DON'T TAKE THEMSELVES SERIOUSLY

OKAY, THEY'RE NOT REALLY BIG STARS, LIKE BARBARA STREISAND OR MICHAEL KNIGHTRIDER BUT THEY'RE PROBABLY MORE FAMOUS THAN YOU. HELL, WILLY FROM 'WHERE'S WILLY' GETS MORE PROPS THAN YOU AND HE'S FAMOUS FOR TRYING TO REMAIN HIDDEN. WHAT HAVE YOU DONE WITH YOUR LIFE? HERE'S AN AD HOC COLLECTION OF SKITS FROM FAMILY GUY TO READ WHILE YOU DOODY.

IN 'DEATH HAS A SHADOW' PAT SUMMERALL STARS AS HIMSELF, ALONGSIDE A TYPICALLY DOWNBEAT JOHN MADDEN.
JM: "THE AIR IS ELECTRIC HERE AT SUPER BOWL XXXIII TONIGHT! PAT, I THINK IT'S SAFE TO SAY THAT ALL THESE FANS CAME OUT HERE TO WATCH A GAME OF FOOTBALL!"
PS: "JOHN, WE'RE IN COMMERCIAL." JOHN: "YEAH, I KNOW. I'M JUST MAKING CONVERSATION. COME ON! (WAVES HIS HANDS IN PAT'S FACE) FOOTBALL!"

IN 'NEVER MET THE DEAD MAN', CHIPS' ERIK ESTRADA STARS AS 'PONCH':
WOMAN: "WHAT'S THE CHARGE, OFFICER?"
ERIK ESTRADA: "DRIVING WITHOUT MY PHONE NUMBER." (GUNSHOTS FIRE). "OR MAYBE I SHOULD ARREST YOU FOR BEING TOO BEAUTIFUL." (TEETH SPARKLE)

IN 'I AM PETER, HEAR ME ROAR' ACTRESS CANDICE BERGEN STARS AS GLORIA IRONBOX, A MILITANT LESBIAN LAWYER.
GI: "MR. GRIFFIN, I'M GLORIA IRONBOX. I REPRESENT ONE OF YOUR CO-WORKERS, SARAH BENNETT. SHE'S SUING YOU AND THE COMPANY FOR SEXUAL HARASSMENT."
PETER: "SARAH, SARAH...I DON'T... OH, IS SHE THE ONE WE VIDEOTAPED TAKING A DUMP? WHY? WHAT HAPPENED?" GI: "SEXUAL HARASSMENT IS A VERY SERIOUS CHARGE, MR. GRIFFIN." PETER: "ALL RIGHT, LOOK, FIRST OF ALL, IF I CAN SPEAK IN MY OWN DEFENCE, ALL I DID WAS TELL A LITTLE JOKE. SECOND OF ALL, WOMEN ARE NOT PEOPLE. THEY ARE DEVICES BUILT BY THE LORD JESUS CHRIST FOR OUR ENTERTAINMENT."

IN 'RUNNING MATES', SIX MILLION FREAKIN' DOLLAR MAN LEE MAJORS STARS AS HIS BIONIC BAD SELF.
LOIS: "CHRIS, WE'LL CONTINUE THIS DISCUSSION TONIGHT YOUNG MAN. A WOMAN IS NOT AN OBJECT."
PETER: "YOUR MOTHER'S RIGHT SON. LISTEN TO WHAT IT SAYS." LOIS: "PETER!"
PETER: "UHHH... I DIDN'T SAY THAT. LEE MAJORS DID." LEE MAJORS: "WHAT? WOMEN ARE THINGS."

IN 'BRIAN DOES HOLLYWOOD', FAMILY GUY GOES X-RATED WHEN JENNA JAMESON AND SAMUEL L JACKSON APPEAR. BRIAN GETS A GIG AS A FILM DIRECTOR, UNBEKNOWNST TO THE GRIFFINS, HE'S DIRECTING SMUT. NOW LOOK AT THAT, UNBEKNOWNST IN A SENTENCE. LOVELY STUFF. JENNA JAMESON: "YES! YES! YES! (HEAVY BREATHING)" BRIAN: CUT. UH, OKAY. NICE TAKE, JENNA. BUT LET'S TRY GIVING THE LINES A LITTLE SUBTEXT THIS TIME. YOUR HUSBAND'S ALWAYS AWAY ON BUSINESS, AND YOU FEEL INCREASINGLY ISOLATED AND UNLOVED. SO YOU BEGIN TO THINK MAYBE YOU SHOULD GO BACK TO GRADUATE SCHOOL AND FINISH YOUR DISSERTATION. AND THAT'S WHEN YOU NOTICE THE CABLE MAN HAS TAKEN HIS PANTS OFF." PETER: "WOW! A REAL MOVIE SET. HEY, THIS HOUSE LOOKS KIND OF FAMILIAR." CHRIS: "I'LL BET SAMUEL L. JACKSON IS HERE. HE'S IN EVERYTHING. THERE'S BRIAN!" BRIAN: "ALRIGHT, NOW SAMUEL, WHEN YOU LAY HER DOWN IN FRONT OF THE FIREPLACE I WANT YOU TO ENTER FROM...OH, MY GOD! HEY, YOU GUYS!" MEG: "HEY, BRIAN? CAN I BE IN THE MOVIE?" PORN PRODUCER: "WELL, ACTUALLY, ONE OF THE JACUZZI GIRLS DIDN'T SHOW UP. HOW LONG CAN YOU HOLD YOUR BREATH UNDERWATER, SWEETIE?"

IN 'STUCK TOGETHER, TORN APART', UBER-ACTRESS JENNIFER LOVE HEWITT STARS AS HERSELF, WITH HILARIOUS EFFECT... JLH: "I KNOW WHAT YOU DID LAST SUMMER?" PETER: "NEVER HEARD OF IT." JLH: "THE DEVIL AND DANIEL WEBSTER?" PETER: "NOPE." JLH: "PARTY OF FIVE?" PETER: "WAS THAT A PORNO? HEY, HEY, DON'T WORRY ABOUT IT. SOMETIMES YOU GOTTA DO A LOT OF CRAP BEFORE THEY PUT YOU IN ANYTHING DECENT. AW, THE FOOD HERE IS FANTASTIC. THIS IS WHERE I TOOK LOIS ON OUR FIRST DATE." JLH: "YOU ORDERED A PIE FOR AN APPETIZER?" PETER: "OH, YEAH, DON'T WORRY. I'LL GO TO THE JOHN AND FIRE ONE OUT IN FIVE MINUTES. THAT SHOULD MAKE ROOM FOR DINNER."

'WHEN YOU WISH UPON A WEINSTEIN' HAS LUKE SKYWALKER IN IT. LUKE SKYWALKER! DID YOU KNOW HIS SEXY DRAG ACT NAME IS MARK HAMILL?
MEG: "MY GLASSES! I CAN'T SEE A THING WITHOUT MY GLASSES! WHY WON'T YOU LET ME GET LASER SURGERY?" LOIS: "BECAUSE I DON'T THINK IT'S SAFE." (CUT TO LUKE SKYWALKER USING HIS LIGHT SABRE FOR EYE SURGERY) LUKE: "OKAY, I JUST NEED TO MAKE A QUICK INCISION HERE AND WE SHOULD BE ALL DONE, MRS. WILSON." OBI-WAN KENOBI: "LUKE, USE THE FORCE." LUKE: "REALLY? 'CAUSE I WAS JUST GONNA MAKE..." OBI-WAN KENOBI: "USE-USE THE FORCE." LUKE: "OKAY!" (PICKS UP LIGHT SABRE WITH THE FORCE, THEN STABS WOMAN THROUGH THE HEAD) LUKE: "ARE YOU HAPPY?" OBI-WAN KENOBI: "I'VE NEVER BEEN HAPPY.

WHEN QUAGMIRE STARTS TO DOUBT HIS PILOTING ABILITIES IN AIRPORT '07, HE TURNS TO PLAYBOY LEGEND HUGH HEFNER FOR SAGELY ADVICE:
HH: "YOU LOOK LIKE YOU GOT SOMETHING ON YOUR MIND." QUAGMIRE: "AH, WHO THE HELL AM I KIDDING? I DON'T DESERVE TO BE A PILOT. I'VE LET EVERYBODY DOWN." HH:

"DID YOU DO THE BEST YOU COULD?" QUAGMIRE: "NO. I WAS GONNA, BUT I ENDED UP GETTING LAID INSTEAD." HH: "THAT REMINDS ME OF A GUY YOU MIGHT'VE HEARD OF. JOHN HOLMES. GREATEST PORN STAR WHO EVER LIVED. YOU KNOW WHAT HE ONCE SAID? HE SAID: 'YOU KNOW, I'VE GOT A 13-INCH MEMBER... AND GLENN QUAGMIRE IS THE BEST DAMN PILOT I'VE EVER SEEN'." QUAGMIRE: "JOHN HOLMES SAID THAT?" HH: "YOU BET HE DID... RIGHT BEFORE HE DIED A VERY PAINFUL, AIDS- RELATED DEATH FROM HAVING UNPROTECTED SEX WITH SO MANY PEOPLE."

IN 'BILL AND PETER'S BOGUS JOURNEY', WE SEE 'JAWS' GUY ROY SCHEIDER'S PROMOTIONAL POOP VIDEO:
ROY: "HI, I'M ROY SCHEIDER. AND TODAY WE'RE GOING TO LEARN TO USE THE POTTY. FOLKS, SAY HI TO MY PAL HUNGRY HANK. HOW'S IT GOING, HANK? HANK: "I'M HUNGRY FOR YOUR POO. DON'T MAKE ME STARVE."

Funny Quotes

PETER

"YOU'D BETTER WATCH WHO YOU'RE CALLING A CHILD, LOIS, BECAUSE IF I'M A CHILD, YOU KNOW WHAT THAT MAKES YOU? A PAEDOPHILE. AND I'LL BE DAMNED IF I'M GONNA BE LECTURED BY A PERVERT."

"OF COURSE A MAN MADE IT. IT'S A COMMERCIAL, LOIS, NOT A DELICIOUS THANKSGIVING DINNER."

"YOUR HONOUR, I CALL TO THE STAND MY SURPRISE WITNESS: THE GHOST THAT NEVER LIES. BUT ONLY I CAN SEE HIM AND HEAR HIM, SO I'LL TELL YOU WHAT HE'S DOING AND SAYING."

"HEY, LOIS, LOOK. THE TWO SYMBOLS OF THE REPUBLICAN PARTY: AN ELEPHANT AND A BIG, FAT WHITE GUY WHO'S THREATENED BY CHANGE."

"GAYS DON'T VOMIT. THEY'RE A VERY CLEAN PEOPLE. AND THEY HAVE BEEN EVER SINCE THEY CAME TO THIS COUNTRY FROM FRANCE."

"MY FATHER'S BEEN WORKING AT THE PLANT FOR 60 YEARS. THAT'S NEARLY 80 YEARS."

STEWIE

"NOT SO HARD, WOMAN! YOU'RE WASHING A BABY'S HAIR, NOT CLEANING THE VOMIT OFF YOUR PARTY DRESS, YOU HOLIDAY DRUNK!"

"YES I WANT A SUNDAE, BUT NO SPRINKLES! FOR EVERY SPRINKLE I FIND...I SHALL KILL YOU!"

"DAMN YOU, VILE WOMAN, YOU'VE IMPEDED MY WORK SINCE THE DAY I ESCAPED YOUR WRETCHED WOMB."

"AHA! SO THEY DO MAKE BIGGER DIAPERS! THAT DECEITFUL WOMAN TOLD ME I'D HAVE TO LEARN TO USE THE TOILET! WELL, FIE ON THE TOILET! IT'S MADE SLAVES OF YOU ALL! I'VE SEEN IT SITTING IN THERE, LAZY, SLOTHFUL, PORCELAIN LAYABOUT FEEDING ON OTHER PEOPLE'S DOO-DOOS WHILE CONTRIBUTING NOTHING OF ITS OWN TO SOCIETY!"

"HEY, MOTHER, I COME BEARING A GIFT. I'LL GIVE YOU A HINT. IT'S IN MY DIAPER AND IT'S NOT A TOASTER."

"HELP! I'VE ESCAPED FROM KEVIN SPACEY'S BASEMENT! HELP ME!"

LOIS

"PETER, I GOT A WAX JOB AND LET'S JUST SAY YOU'RE CLEARED FOR LANDING!"

CLEVELAND

"HEY, BABY. HOW WOULD YOU LIKE TO GO BLACK, AND THEN MAKE A DIFFICULT DECISION REGARDING WHETHER OR NOT TO GO BACK?"

BRIAN

"I'M NOT DRUNK! I JUST HAVE SPEECH IMPEDIMENT... AND A STOMACH VIRUS... AND AN INNER EAR INFECTION."

"WELL, PETER, IF YOU PLAN TO PULL A PARTY OUT OF YOUR ASS, YOU BETTER STAND UP."

QUAGMIRE

"HELLO, 911? IT'S QUAGMIRE. YEAH, IT'S CAUGHT IN THE WINDOW THIS TIME."

CHRIS

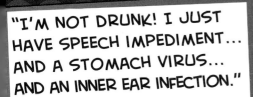

"I JUST WANT PEACE ON EARTH. THAT'S BETTER THAN BEING SELFISH LIKE MEG, RIGHT? SO I SHOULD GET MORE THAN HER."

TOM TUCKER

"A BIT OF BREAKING NEWS. A LOCAL FAMILY IS FORCED OUT OF THEIR HOME BY GHOSTS. WHO ARE THEY GONNA CALL? THEIR INSURANCE COMPANY."

GLENN PROFILE & QUAGMIRE INTERVIEW

Hic-a-doo-La!

That Special Feeling

115

GLENN QUAGMIRE

GLENN QUAGMIRE OPENLY ADMITTED THAT IF HE COULD SPEND THE REST OF HIS LIFE WITH ANY WOMAN ON A DESERT ISLAND IT WOULD BE TAYLOR HANSON FROM HANSON. WHEN HE WAS TOLD HANSON WAS A GUY, HE REPLIED: "YOU GUYS ARE YANKIN' ME. 'HEY, LET'S PUT ONE OVER ON QUAGMIRE'. WHAT? THAT'S INSANE. THAT'S IMPOSSIBLE. OH GOD. OH MY GOD. I'VE GOT ALL THESE MAGAZINES... OH GOD."

EVEN GLENN'S MOTHER IS NOT SAFE FROM THE MAN'S HERCULEAN LIBIDO. WHEN TV PROGRAMME 'THE BACHELORETTE' CAME TO QUAHOG, WHILE IN THE FINAL, QUAGMIRE TOOK THE SHOW'S ONLY WOMAN, BROOKE, HOME TO MEET HIS MOTHER. AFTER A SHORT ARGUMENT HE SHOUTED: "MOM, YOU WANT THIS THREE-WAY TO HAPPEN, YOU'RE GOING TO HAVE TO CHANGE YOUR TONE."

CAN YOU BELIEVE THE QUAG WAS ONCE ALMOST MARRIED, TO THAT MANIAC, JOAN? AFTER SEEING LOIS' ENGORGED BREASTS, QUAGMIRE KNEW HE COULDN'T MARRY JOAN, SO PETER ENACTED PLAN A, A FOOL-PROOF SCHEME TO SHOW JOAN A VIDEO OF QUAGMIRE BEING KILLED. HIS ASSAILANTS? A HANDICAPPED NINJA (JOE), NAZI WITH A RAY GUN (CLEVELAND), POTS-AND-PANS ROBOT (PETER) AND A DINOSAUR. IT DIDN'T WORK. BUT IT COULD HAVE, EASILY COULD HAVE.

ACCORDING TO VOICE AND CREATOR SETH MACFARLANE, GLENN QUAGMIRE WAS BASED ON 'A FIFTIES RADIO GUY ON COKE'. ON THAT THEME, QUAGMIRE'S HOUSE IS REMINISCENT OF A SWINGING SIXTIES PARTY WITH A BED HIDDEN IN NEARLY EVERY PART OF HIS HOUSE.

QUAGMIRE WAS BASED ON THE FACIAL CHARACTERISTICS OF BOB HOPE – CLEFT CHIN AND LONG, POINTY NOSE. HE USUALLY WEARS GARISH HAWAIIAN SHIRTS, A GOLD MEDALLIAN, AND AN ERECTION.

QUAGMIRE IS ONE OF LIFE'S HAPPY NECROPHILIACS: IN 'I TAKE THEE QUAGMIRE', WHEN DEATH ACCIDENTLY KILLED JOAN, GLENN ASKS DEATH IF HE COULD LEAVE THE BODY WITH HIM FOR FIVE MINUTES. FIVE MINUTES. THAT'S ALL THE TIME THE MAN NEEDS... WITH A DEAD BODY. GIGITTY GHOULISH.

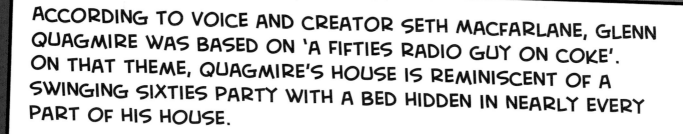

FACTFILE

AGE: 61

PLACE OF BIRTH:
QUAHOG, RHODE ISLAND

BIRTH NAME:
GLENN QUAGMIRE

GENDER: ALL MAN

MEET... GLEN QUAGMIRE

GLEN QUAGMORE IS A BUSY MAN, A LADIES MAN WITH THE NOSE OF A BLOODHOUND AND THE EYE OF A TIGER.

HE DOESN'T TAKE NO FOR AN ANSWER AND EVEN CONSIDERS HIS BEST FRIENDS' WIVES FAIR GAME – INCLUDING AN EXTRA-MARITAL AFFAIR WITH LORETTA.

HE'S PRETTY OBSESSED WITH LOIS AND HAS BEEN CAUGHT SPYING ON HER AND MADE PASSES AT HER WHEN HE THOUGHT HER AND PETER WERE SPLITTING UP.

GLEN HAS LITTLE INTEREST IN LONG-TERM RELATIONSHIPS WITH WOMEN. HE IS THE ORIGINAL SEX-CRAZED, PERVERTED NEIGHBOUR.

HE ONCE RAN TO THE RESCUE OF A PARTIALLY-NAKED WOMAN IN A DRESSING ROOM WHO WAS HAVING A HEART ATTACK. HE RUBBED HER CHEST AND BREATHED DEEPLY INTO HER MOUTH TO REVIVE HER... OH, AND DON'T FORGET HIS FOOT FETISH!

AND IF YOU HEAR THE WORDS "GIGGITY GIGGITY GOO" YOU KNOW THAT GLEN IS ABOUT TO HAVE THOUGHTS – AT THE VERY LEAST – ABOUT HIS FAVOURITE PASTIME.

YOU WONT MISS HIM EITHER IN HIS BRIGHT SHIRTS, OFTEN HAWAIIAN IN STYLE. AND WATCH OUT FOR THE BEDS HIDDEN IN EVERY ROOM OF HIS HOUSE!

THE LIFE AND TIMES OF GLEN QUAGMIRE

AUCTIONEER: OUR FIRST ITEM IS A PAIR OF PANTIES CONFISCATED FROM A PROSTITUTE.

QUAGMIRE: FIFTY BUCKS.

AUCTIONEER: SHE HAD NINE STDS.

QUAGMIRE: FORTY-FIVE BUCKS.

AUCTIONEER: AND WHEN WE CAUGHT HER SHE WET HERSELF.

QUAGMIRE: FIFTY BUCKS.

QUAGMIRE: HELLO, 911? IT'S QUAGMIRE. YEAH, IT'S CAUGHT IN THE WINDOW THIS TIME.

SOCIAL WORKER: "GLEN HONEY, I GOT A QUESTION FOR YOU. WHAT DO YOU DO FOR A LIVING?

QUAGMIRE: "I GOT A QUESTION FOR YOU. WHY ARE YOU STILL HERE?"

QUAGMIRE: FAT CHICKS NEED LOVE TOO...THEY JUST HAVE TO PAY!

PETER: IF YOU COULD BE STRANDED ON A DESERT ISLAND WITH ANY WOMAN IN THE WORLD, WHO WOULD IT BE?

QUAGMIRE: TAYLOR HANSON.

JOE SWANSON: TAYLOR HANSON IS A GUY.

QUAGMIRE: YOU GUYS ARE YANKIN' ME. "HEY, LET'S PUT ONE OVER ON QUAGMIRE."

PETER: NO, HE'S ACTUALLY A GUY, QUAGMIRE.

QUAGMIRE: WHAT? THAT'S INSANE. THAT'S IMPOSSIBLE. OH GOD. OH MY GOD. I'VE GOT ALL THESE MAGAZINES. OH GOD.

BROOKE: QUAGMIRE, WILL YOU ACCEPT THIS ROSE?

QUAGMIRE: REALLY? AFTER I DRUGGED YOU AND HAD SEX WITH YOUR UNCONSCIOUS BODY?

BROOKE: WHAT?

QUAGMIRE: YES.

TRICIA TAKANAWA: SEX. SOME PEOPLE HAVE IT ANONYMOUSLY. WHAT KIND OF PERSON WOULD DO THAT YOU MIGHT ASK? WELL, I'M ABOUT TO FIND OUT. I'VE JUST PICKED UP A COMPLETE STRANGER IN A HOTEL BAR AND HE'S IN THE BATHROOM RIGHT NOW, POSSIBLY DOING

DRUGS. WATCH AS I HAVE SEX WITH THIS POTENTIALLY DANGEROUS MAN, AS WE TAKE YOU IN-DEPTH AND UNDERCOVER.

QUAGMIRE: I'VE NEVER HAD A SPANISH CHICK BEFORE! O-LE!

QUAGMIRE: HERE'S TO THE DRUNKEN CLAM, WHERE THEY

DON'T ASK FOR PROOF OF AGE AND NEITHER DO I.

PETER: I'M GONNA GO MICROWAVE A BAGEL AND HAVE SEX WITH IT.

QUAGMIRE: BUTTER'S IN THE FRIDGE!

QUAGMIRE: HEY GUYS, WHAT'S GOING ON? I WAS JUST JERKI... ED OUT OF A DEEP SLEEP.

QUIZ
BASED ON STORYLINES AND PLOTS

SO, YOU'VE BEEN SAT THERE, TITTERING LIKE SOME SORT OF NEGLECTFUL, SWAG-BELLIED MOTHER OF THREE, YOUR SNOUT CRAMMED INTO SPITTLED-FLECKED PAGES AS YOUR GIN-SOAKED BREATH REBOUNDS FROM ITS PAGES.

WELL, YE SHALL LAUGH NO MORE! IT IS TIME TO PUT YOUR HOURS, DAYS AND WEEKS PERCHED IN FRONT OF TELEVISIONS, DVDS AND CARTOON ANNUALS TO THE ULTIMATE TEST WITH QUESTIONS SO FIENDISH THEY COULD BE JOSEPH GOEBBELS' MORE FIENDISH, BUT PAINFULLY SHY BROTHER.

I DARE YOU TO ANSWER THESE QUESTIONS. WERE YOU TO ANSWER ALL 25 CORRECTLY, I DO NOT NEED TO HUNT YOU DOWN AS YOU WILL NO DOUBT BE ATTRACTING THE ATTENTION OF THE AUTHORITIES SOON ENOUGH...

1. IN 'STEWIE LOVES LOIS', WHAT DOES PETER CALL HIMSELF IN THE SCENE, POST PROSTATE EXAM, WHERE HE IS CUTTING OFF HIS HAIR IN THE BATHROOM?

2. WHAT IS THE NAME OF THE GIANT CHICKEN THAT PETER FIGHTS?

3. IN 'MEET THE QUAGMIRES' WHO DOES PETER MARRY INSTEAD OF LOIS?

4. IN 'A PICTURE'S WORTH A THOUSAND BUCKS', WHAT WAS THE NAME CHRIS USED WHEN HE WAS AN ARTIST?

5. IN SEASON FOUR, PETER STARTS HIS OWN RELIGION, WHO DOES HE WORSHIP?

6. HOW DID STEWIE GET HIS CRUELLY MISSHAPEN RUGBY BALL HEAD?

7. BEFORE MEETING PETER, LOIS HAD SEX WITH KISS LEAD SINGER GENE SIMMONS, WHAT WAS HIS NICKNAME FOR HER?

8. IN SEASON FIVE'S 'ROAD TO RUPERT', WHO PROVIDES THE VOICE FOR THE GRIFFIN'S MOVING AWAY NEIGHBOUR STANFORD CORDRAY?

9. IN 'BILL AND PETER'S BOGUS JOURNEY', WHO IS BILL?

10. IN 'MEALS NO WHEELS', WHAT IS THE NAME OF THE WHEELCHAIR TRANSFORMER CREATED BY THE GRIFFIN'S DISGRUNTLED CUSTOMERS?

11. WHICH CELEBRITY TOOK MEG'S VIRGINITY?

12. IN 'BLUE HARVEST', WHO PLAYS C-3PO?

13. IN 'MCSTROKE', WHAT DOES PETER RECEIVE FOR HELPING TO SAVE MCBURGERTOWN FROM BURNING DOWN?

14. WHICH FILM IS REFERENCED AT THE END OF 'PETER'S GOT WOODS' AND 'BACK TO THE WOODS'?

15. IN 'BRIAN: PORTRAIT OF A DOG' WHY DOES BRIAN PERFORM TRICKS AT A DOG SHOW?

16. IN '420', WHAT DO BRIAN AND STEWIE LEGALISE?

17. WHAT SONG DOES STEWIE SING TO WOO SUSIE SWANSON IN 'OCEAN'S THREE AND A HALF'?

18. WITH WHOM DOES STEWIE SPEND THE WHOLE DAY IN 'NOT ALL DOGS GO TO HEAVEN'?

19. IN 'I DREAM OF JESUS', WHERE DOES PETER MEET THE SON OF GOD?

20. WHAT KIND OF PEOPLE DID LOIS' LONG LOST BROTHER PATRICK PEWTERSCHMIDT LIKE KILLING?

21. IN 'WASTED TALENT', WHAT INSTRUMENT DOES PETER FIND HE CAN PLAY BRILLIANTLY WHEN DRUNK?

22. WHAT IS THE NAME OF THE CHICK FLICK THAT PETER MAKES IN 'CHICK CANCER'.

23. WHERE IS A WOMAN'S 'FOURTH HOLE' THAT QUAGMIRE FINDS ON HIS DATE IN 'MEET THE QUAGMIRES'?

24. IN 'AIRPORT '07', WHY DID QUAGMIRE LOSE HIS JOB?

25. ACCORDING TO THE CONVERSATION IN 'FISH OUT OF WATER', WHO WOULD PETER HAVE IF HE WERE NOT MARRIED TO LOIS?

PAGE 40

1. IRON MAN
2. COCO
3. PRINCESS LEIA
4. FIORG VAN DER PLOEG
5. HERBERT
6. SHAMUS
7. ELIZA
8. LOIS' RIVAL PIANO TEACHER
9. WATCHES YOU PEE
10. HIS OWN HAND (AND DO YOU KNOW SHE CHATS ON HIM?)
11. CHRISTIAN THE SKINNY TERMINATOR BALE
12. SETH ROGEN
13. CONWAY TWITTY, AND I FREAKIN WELL LOVED THAT CLOP
14. MICHAEL MOORE
15. YOUNGBLOOD. SEXY YOUNGBLOOD
16. DR. WHO
17. NORM FROM CHEERS
18. MARY-KATE OLSEN
19. NAPOLEON DYNAMITE
20. MORT GOLDMAN

PAGE 122

1. FILTHY WHORE!
2. ERNIE
3. MOLLY RINGWORM (SORRY, RINGWALD).
4. CHRISTOBEL
5. THE FONZ
6. CRASHING INTO THE CEILING WHILE BOUNCING ON THE BED
7. LOOSE LOIS
8. ROB LOWE
9. BILL CLINTON
10. CRIPPLETRON
11. JIMMY FALLON
12. QUAGMIRE
13. UNLIMITED BURGERS, WHICH IS WHY HE HAS THE STROKE, DUMB ASS.
14. RAIDERS OF THE LOST ARK
15. TO EARN MONEY FOR AIR CONDITIONING
16. MARIJUANA. BABY.
17. EVERYTHING I DO BY BRYAN ADAMS
18. THE CAST OF STAR TREK: NEXT GENERATION
19. AT THE RECORD STORE
20. FAT FOLKS
21. PIANO
22. STEEL VAGINAS
23. BACK OF THE KNEE. GIGGITY.
24. PETER STOLE FUEL FOR HIS NEW PICK UP, TAKING IT FROM QUAGMIRE'S AIRCRAFT
25. THE CHICK FROM TOTAL RECALL WITH THREE KNOCKERS